THE HERBAL YEAR BOOK

Herbalists Without Borders Bristol

activedistribution.org

Bristol, England

First print, October 2022

ISBN 978 1 914567 17 9

Contents

3

Calendula
Belle Benfield / bellebenfield.com

Introduction

Herbalists Without Borders Bristol (HWBB) is a collaboration between volunteers who are passionate about plant medicine, including clinical herbalists, community herbalists, herb growers, and local support projects that work with asylum seekers and refugees in Bristol. We are allied with Herbalist Without Borders Calais[1].

Since 2017 we have been supporting seven refugee projects in Bristol, which we talk about in more detail below. We do this with a mobile dispensary of herbal medicines that are free at the point of delivery for common ailments such as: insomnia, anxiety, coughs and low immunity. We are entirely self funded and to date we have been able to offer these medicines for free. This has been possible largely through the sales of our calendars and our harvesting wall chart. The first two calendars gave tips on wild harvesting or 'wildcrafting' through the year and the third one was focused on monthly herb gardening. The book you are holding is based on those calendars but we have also added new information, recipes and artwork.

---

[1] *hwbcalais.org*

Our roots

In 2015/2016 a huge exodus of people fled Syria. The refugee camps in Calais and Dunkirk swelled with people arriving on a daily basis. Around this time, Herbalists without Borders Calais was set up. Here in Bristol, we wanted to be able to respond locally, so we set up HWBB in the summer of 2016. Setting up the project was a deeply rooted act of resistance against an unjust global political system that has created border politics that entrench inequalities and injustices that are difficult to ignore.

Since the inception of the project, the politics of immigration in the UK have become even less humane. The government is actively hostile to the plight of those named as immigrants/asylum seekers/refugees.

This 'hostile environment' has introduced regulations that require ID checks for all patients accessing most secondary (non-emergency) care. This includes, but is not limited to, maternity/ante-natal care, paediatrics and cancer treatment. NHS Trusts are forced to assess eligibility for treatment and charge upfront those who cannot provide ID. These regulations follow the introduction of a Health Surcharge – paid on top of visa application fees. Both policies were introduced following the 2014 and 2016 Immigrations Acts[2]. Two of the organisations which are trying to highlight and campaign against these changes are Patients not Passports[3] and Docs not Cops[4]. Like us, they believe that health is a right and not a privilege.

These changes in policies have in turn created even more vulnerability and fear in migrant communities. A recent study showed that fewer refugees were seeking NHS health care than previously, as they were afraid of this 'hostility'.

---

[2] *Source: Docs not Cops*
[3] *www.patientsnotpassports.co.uk*
[4] *www.docsnotcops.co.uk*

HWBB is part of the broader resistance to this 'hostile environment'. We want to contribute to the dismantling of borders within healthcare. As one of our volunteers recently said, "what we do is important, part of it is giving out the herbs but the other is turning up each month and being here as an act of solidarity".

As a project we don't ask for anyone's personal details, 'papers' or 'immigration status'. We try to provide healthcare while treating each person with the dignity and respect that they deserve. We believe that herbal medicine is an important part of any healthcare system and can have profound effects individually, as a community, and in wider society.

How does herbal medicine help people?

Some of the challenges that people face who have fled their homes include: homelessness, unstable housing, poverty, ill health, loneliness and social isolation. In addition, there is often a constant state of uncertainty regarding one's future and asylum status as well as the detrimental impacts of ongoing structural inequalities and racism. Living in such stressful conditions greatly impacts health and wellbeing, creating high levels of anxiety and trauma. The impact of all these stressors can manifest as chronic insomnia, depleted immunity leading to infections of all kinds, digestive issues, injuries that won't heal, as well as other more complex conditions.

Herbal medicine has a lot to offer in treating all of these illnesses, and herbs can help build resilience to prevent future illness. We often support whole families including the children. The people we meet have really welcomed our presence when we visit the projects. Partly, this is due to the fact that herbal medicine is a familiar healthcare choice in the countries that people have come from. Also, the consistency of us being there every month has built relationships and trust. We often exchange stories of native plants and their uses. It is our hope that we will continue to collaborate and document this sharing.

What we do

In addition to the delivery of free medicine in the refugee projects, HWBB can be accessed in various different ways. For example, growing herbs, local herb walks or self-care workshops. All of which can play a vital part in improving health and wellbeing. Connecting people with plants and nature in Bristol is an important part of helping people to feel at home in an alien urban environment.

We organise:

- A mobile dispensary for common ailments, such as: insomnia, anxiety, coughs and low immunity. This dispensary is taken to existing support drop-in projects in the city.

- Supplying support projects with packs of herbs to give out to their clients, e.g. Immunity Pack/Stress Pack/Sleep Pack. This was important during the pandemic when drop-in centres were closed.

- Collaborating with support projects in Bristol to deliver self-care and medicine making workshops.

- Regular gardening sessions at our medicine garden.

- Harvesting of herbs from local growing projects including the HWBB medicine garden.

- Wildcrafting events to harvest herbs.

- Volunteer medicine making events where we make the medicines for the mobile clinics.

We visit four different projects every month

- Borderlands is a charity that works with asylum seekers and refugees (*www.borderlands.uk.com*).

- Bristol Hospitality Network works for asylum seekers facing destitution by sourcing hosted accommodation and fostering creative community engagement across Bristol *(www.bhn.org.uk)*.

- Refugee Women of Bristol specifically targets the needs of refugee women in Bristol *(www.refugeewomenofbristol.org.uk)*.

- Since 2022, we have been visiting a group of Afghani women who have been staying in hotels around Bristol while they are waiting to be housed.

The three other projects that we support are Project Mama, AidBox and Unseen. We go to these projects less frequently than monthly, deliver workshops or make up packages for them to give out.

- Project Mama is a charitable organisation that particularly supports women refugees, asylum-seekers, those with uncertain immigration status and survivors of modern slavery and human trafficking. Project Mama focuses on this demographic because of the extreme difficulty women can have accessing the NHS, the language barriers they face and the extreme social isolation they may experience. They offer support for pregnancy, labour and childbirth and antenatal support *(www.projectmama.org)*.

- Unseen is an anti-slavery charity that supports victims of human trafficking and modern slavery in the form of safe houses and community support *(www.unseenuk.org)*.

- AidBox is an organisation that supports and provides supplies to refugees and asylum seekers through a free shop and community hub *(www.aidboxcommunity.co.uk)*.

Colonialism and the UK's role in worldwide injustice

We believe that it is of the utmost importance to acknowledge the devastating impact of the UK's history of colonialism and racism as having ongoing and devastating impacts. The UK's foreign policy and arms trade deals contribute to the factors that force so many people to leave their war-torn countries in search of a life where they can live, work and breathe without the fear of persecution. We stand in solidarity with all those resisting unjust borders regimes and systems that only allow those will wealth to migrate.

If you want to read more about the history of the UK's involvement in creating mass migrations of people here are a few suggestions:

- *Natives, Race & Class in the Ruins of the Empire,* by Akala (Two Roads 2019)
- *Against Borders, the case for abolition,* by Gracie Mae Bradley and Luke de Noronha (Verso Press 2022)
- *How Britain Broke the World: War, Greed and Blunders from Kosovo to Afghanistan, 1997-2021,* by Arthur Snell (Canbury Press 2022)
- *(B)ordering Britain: Law, Race and Empire,* by Nadine El-Enany (Manchester University Press 2020)

Colonialism, decolonisation and herbal medicine

The impact of colonialism is systemic and as such is woven through all aspects of our society, including the herbal world. There is now an active campaign to decolonise herbal medicine which involves acknowledging the history of how plants from all over the world have been incorporated into 'western' herbal medicine. The sharing of knowledge globally was not always done in an equitable way and the stories of many previous injustices, like the colonial struggles that occurred in India and China, can be found in our herbal medicine chests today. Many of our medicinal plants are tied up with this unacknowledged colonial history.

Some of the herbs that we use in the UK come from North America, the knowledge of which was shared with the first colonisers. But was this an equal exchange? Were Native American tribes credited for the medicinal knowledge? Who profited from sharing this stolen knowledge? Do we acknowledge the genocide that occurred when the Americas were first colonised?

One of the ways we can start to decolonise 'western' herbal medicine is by opening up this conversation and asking questions about all the herbs that we use.

Indigenous herbal knowledge is still very much under threat. In solidarity with those that stand against the continuous theft of traditional knowledge, we need to educate ourselves about the land struggles that are still happening now. At the moment, there is resistance by First Nation tribes to challenge the ongoing expansion of tar sands into their lands[5].

The Herbal Anthropology Project is involved in projects that ally with indigenous people to record and preserve traditional medicines that are under threat from land theft, migration, and continuing loss of traditional culture[6].

The legacy of colonialism and present day market capitalism are evident in the global herb trade. It is important to think about the source of the herbs that we buy from abroad and the impact of their production on the environment, fair trade and employment rights etc. One way to assess whether a company is working in an inclusive, equitable and regenerative way is to see if they are registered as a B corp[7].

---

[5] www.ienearth.org/what-are-the-tar-sands
[6] www.herbalanthropology.org
[7] www.bcorporation.uk

By growing and harvesting your own herbs to use, you can take herbal medicine out of the capitalist chain altogether. In this book we have compiled all the information you need to start wild harvesting, growing and making your own medicine. Throughout the book we have referenced various other useful books and sources to help you to delve deeper into these topics.

"Hands"

About this book

When we initially set up Herbalists Without Borders Bristol, many people offered to harvest or grow herbs for us. We saw this as a way of cutting costs and moving towards self-sufficiency. To support this, we soon realised the need to share our knowledge of which herbs could be wild harvested or grown in the UK. This inspired the first of our calendars. The calendars have been hugely successful and people still ask to buy them even when they are out of date. This made us realise a book was needed!

This book is a year in plants: wild and cultivated. We introduce you, month by month, to some of our valued plants in all their practical value, magic and glory. Each month offers a list of herbs to forage and grow. For the herbs that cannot be collected in the wild, we have also included seasonal herb gardening tips based on our experience of running a community herb garden. Finally, we introduce you to key herbs by sharing some of our favourite recipes.

The writing in this book is a compilation of many people's knowledge. They have brought together the harvesting lists, the botanical know-ledge and the recipes. All of this is accompanied by beautiful drawings that have been donated by an amazing community of artists and plant lovers. We are very grateful to members of the local refugee com-munity who have contributed artwork and recipes. We hope that through these writings, recipes and drawings you will come to love these plants as much as we do.

All proceeds from this book will go towards the work of providing free herbal medicine to refugee projects in Bristol. We continue to do this work as the politics of immigration in the UK become increas-ingly troubling and the need for resistance to the deeply embedded systems of oppression becomes more and more evident. All of our work is voluntary, the medicines are made by volunteers and some of the herbs are grown in our medicine garden in St Werburghs, Bristol.

Harvesting

Wildcrafting

Wildcrafting is the practice of harvesting plants in the wild. It can be done in meditative solitude or with family or friends. The beauty of wildcrafting is that it is free which can make herbal medicine very financially accessible. Another element of wildcrafting is the connection with nature and the seasons. It can help you learn about our beautiful biodiversity and mark a change in time.

Humans used to need to be very attuned to the turning of the year and had rituals and festivals to honour and acknowledge the changes of the seasons. Delving into the wild can bring back that medicine of locating yourself in your ever changing environment.

We hope this book will give enough information and inspiration for you to go out and wildcraft some herbs to make into medicines. We also hope that we can encourage people to carefully wildcraft some of the common herbs we use often in our mobile medicine cart and donate to the project, so we can continue to function in as sustainable a way as possible.

Sustainability

It is very important not to over-harvest because this can put plants in danger of extinction in the wild. This has happened to some of the important North American herbs like Echinacea, Goldenseal, Black Cohosh and American Ginseng. United Plant Savers was set up by herbalist Rosemary Gladstar to promote the preservation of wild herbs[8].

In the UK, loss of habitat is the main reason some plants are becoming endangered. It is important to be as conscious and ethical as possible and only wildcraft common plants. The rule of thumb is to never take more than a third of what you can see and to leave the habitat looking as if you had never been there. If it is a rare plant, do not harvest it. Some of the rarer plants can be cultivated in the garden and we talk more about this in the section on gardening.

The Botanical Society for Britain and Ireland encourages the public to map plant sightings and their reports include a 'red list' of endangered species. If you are unsure whether something is endangered check with them. If something is not very common in the wild, don't harvest it but try to grow it instead.

If you are harvesting on any cultivated land like farms or orchards it is important to get the owner's consent. However, one of our very common yet potent medicinal roots 'Yellow Dock' is on the noxious weeds list so farmers are legally obliged to remove it from their land, therefore harvesting these roots could be helpful!

In this book we distinguish between roots that are very common and tenacious, which can be picked in the wild (such as Dandelion and Horseradish), and those that are rarer and should be cultivated (such as Elecampane, Valerian and Marshmallow).

Where to harvest

Do not harvest near polluted busy roads, rail tracks, park fences, or close to cultivated fields and fruit orchards (unless organically cultivated). The herbs will be affected by chemical contamination through

---

[8] *www.unitedplantsavers.org*

vehicle emissions, creosote, herbicides and pesticides. Take care when harvesting plants growing near or in water – there may be agricultural or industrial runoff upstream.

When to harvest

It is good to observe the lifecycle of the plant: in spring the sap rises and the bark is easy to peel before the leaves unfold. The leaves and flowers are picked as they unfurl, then as the energy goes to the fruit and seeds in the autumn you pick these and finally as the reserves of the plant go back down to the root you harvest these.

Flowers: these are collected just before or when they have fully blossomed. Do not wash flowers - shake to get insects off.

Leaves: gathered when fully developed before the flower blossoms unless you want them with the flowers.

Roots: roots of perennial plants should be dug in late autumn after the aerial parts have died back. You should wait for 2-3 years growth so they mature before you harvest them. For biennial plants, harvest roots in the first autumn.

Bark: harvest in spring or autumn. Take bark from small branches or pruned branches. Never fully ring a tree as this will kill it. Usually the inner bark is needed, which can be hard to separate from the outer bark, so just use all the peeled bark.

Fruit and Seeds: harvest in the autumn. Seeds are the least perishable part of the plant, so can be picked when they are mature on the plant. Nettle seeds are an exception and need to be picked when bright green.

Do not harvest or ingest anything if you are not 100% certain what it is.

Drying and storing

Dry herbs in a warm, dry spot with some airflow in the room. Lay the herbs flat, chopped into small pieces if a root or bark. We like using muslin, either pinned onto wooden frames or across vegetable crates or hung from a low ceiling. A dehydrator can be useful for small spaces. Avoid drying in damp places as the herbs may go mouldy.

Plants are dry enough to be placed in storage only when all the parts are brittle. All parts must snap crisply when bent. You can store your dried herbs in glass, ceramic or metal tins. Check for any condensation in the storage jar a couple of days later to see if herbs are really dry. If the herbs are no longer brittle, take out and dry for longer.

Seasons can shift each year and vary with latitude and altitude. There is sometimes a regrowth of the common spring herbs like Cleavers in the autumn before everything dies back. This book's harvesting information is based on our knowledge of south west England, but if you are more west or north then the season might be up to a month later in spring and summer. The parts of the plant that should be harvested and used are noted. Aerial parts means leaf, stem and flower.

Some herbs can be found in the wild but if they are uncommon we have put them in the cultivated list instead.

The lists in each month are not exhaustive but include the main herbs that we wildcraft and use.

Useful plant books

*   *Wild Flower Guide and Trees in Britain, Europe and North America*, by Roger Phillips

*   *Hedgerow Medicine & Wayside Medicine,*
    by Julie and Matthew Bruton Seal

*   *The Wild Flower Key,*
    by Francis Rose

*   *The Medicinal Flora of Britain and Northwestern Europe,*
    by Julian Barker

Gardening

Not everything we need for the project can be wildcrafted, so we also rely on things we can grow in a herb garden. This section of the book comes from our 2021 herb gardening calendar.

Herbalists Without Borders medicine garden

In 2012, a group of plant lovers and herbalists set up St Werburghs Medicine Garden on an allotment site. It took about two years to clear the site of carpet (NEVER use it for mulching), brambles and Couch Grass. Nicole Vosper, from Solidarity Apothecary, drew up a plan based on body systems. Horticulturist Eleanor Fairbraida then designed each bed according to herb size and other specifics. The beds were covered with mypex to suppress the weeds and leaf mulch was added. Each bed was then planted with the appropriate herbs.

It has taken us many years and hundreds of volunteers to get the garden looking as glorious as it does now. We host regular volunteer sessions where the wider community comes to help us with the work of gardening, harvesting and making medicines. In 2017 it was decided that all the herbs from the allotment would go to Herbalists without Borders Bristol. With this decision we then started to prioritise the planting of herbs that are used in our remedies.

Growing herbs

Growing herbs is a great way to gather the plants that are rare, less common, or not easy to find in the wild. It is also a wonderful way to learn more about each plant. By growing your own herbs you can taste them through the different seasons and this can help you to notice the changes in the herb and decide the best time to harvest. You will be rewarded with a basketful of great quality herbs for your efforts. You'll learn about the herbs' lifecycle, the insects that they attract and which herbs grow well together. Herb growing is also much easier than growing vegetables as herbs do not need as much attention!

Understanding garden basics

Annuals are herbs that will need to be planted each year. These plants grow from seed, come to flower and make seeds, then die all in a single growing season. Some will drop seeds from the year before but you may need to grow more plants.

Examples: Chamomile, Fennel, Californian Poppy, Calendula, Borage, Nasturtium.

Biennials are plants that take two growing seasons to complete their life cycle. In the first year they grow leaves and in the second year they flower and die. If it is the root you need then you will need to harvest in autumn of the first year or spring of the second year.

Examples: Angelica, Burdock, Caraway, Parsley, Mullein (can be short-lived perennial).

Perennial herbs grow bigger each year and mainly look after themselves. They can be grown from seed, root division or cuttings. Dead-heading, weeding around them and cutting back in late autumn are the main jobs that need to be done. If you are going to use the root then you should wait until at least the third year.

Examples: Lavender, Elecampane, Lemon Balm, Wormwood, Agrimony, Skullcap.

Soil type

Soil type refers to the composition of the soil: clay, silt, chalk, sand, peat, or loam. The ideal soil is loamy which is a balance of soil components. Clay soils are nutrient-dense and hold water. Sandy soils are fast draining but will crack open in the summer and don't hold nutrients. Plants have a preferred soil that they thrive in so consider the soil type preference before you plant. Many herbs are resilient and will grow in any soil. The soil in the medicine garden is thick clay and even the Mediterranean herbs that prefer sandy soils do well. Even so, we have been slowly trying to break up the thick clay by adding leaf mulch every year or twice a year. All soil can be improved with a layer of leaf mulch to balance it.

Shade or sun-loving plants

You need to consider whether the plants need
some shade or like full sun, and try to plant
accordingly.

Which method of gardening?

There are lots of methods that could work for a herb garden. Is it going to be no-dig, organic, biodynamic? Read up on this and choose which works for you and your plot.

Planning the garden

People often ask us where they should start when making a herb garden. This is a really big question and we have listed some books that will help you dive in more deeply. The most important thing is to choose plants that you will use and that you will enjoy. Then it's about the space, amount of light/shade, type of soil, and whether plants are perennials/annuals.

Some things to consider

Accessibility to plants: beds should be ideally 3-4 foot wide.

Don't plant very similar herbs next to each other as they can hybridise, for example, Mints, Lavenders, Dill and Fennel.

Think about how the sun moves around and the height of the plants so that you do not plant tall plants that can cast large shadows over smaller plants.

Do the plants like getting their 'feet' wet like Meadowsweet, Irises and Sweet Flag? Adding a small pond can help with this. You can plant the herbs in or around it.

Go slowly, choose a few herbs and get these established, then keep on adding each year.

And finally, don't be afraid to experiment. Every year we move some herbs around to find the best spot. Move the plants in the autumn or early spring.

When we started the medicine garden the beds were divided into body systems, such as the nervous system, respiratory system, immune system. As the project evolves so does the garden. Some of the beds are now given over to one or two herbs we use a lot in our medicines, such as Marshmallow and Mullein, Thyme and Coltsfoot, as well as herbs that support the nervous system such as Skullcap, Wood Betony, Vervain, Chamomile.

Growing in small spaces

You don't need a garden in order to grow herbs, many are happy in pots and containers and you can also grow plants vertically to maximise space. Things to consider when growing in pots:
- Good drainage holes, consider raising them off the ground as this will help.
- Size of the pot: if the plant is small do not plant into too big a pot - it is better to increase the pot size each year.
- Consider the soil: most herbs will do well in a peat-free multipurpose compost.
- Feed plants in pots as they will use up all the nutrients (see April recipe).
- They also need more watering than plants in beds.
- Herbs to consider for small spaces: Calendula, Lavender, Rosemary, Thyme, Skullcap, Basil.

How to care for herbs

How much you should feed your plants is a contested point. As you cultivate herbs there will be a steady depletion of nutrients, so it is important that you add some organic matter such as compost to replenish the soil. Adding horse manure to the soil can help produce big luscious herbs, but from a medicinal perspective these herbs may be too well nourished. This is because plants produce secondary metabolites, a group of compounds that help them to survive in difficult conditions, and it is these secondary metabolites that are medicine to us. It is thought that if the plant is too well fed it will produce less of these secondary metabolites and perhaps be less medicinal. It's all about finding a balance, and working with the conditions.

Herbs need to be watered, but less often than vegetables. If they are perennials with an established root system then they are going to be more hardy than annuals. Seedlings need to be watered often, so remember that when you are planting them out. Don't let the weeds get out of hand. Annuals require regular weeding, but perennials can also get overwhelmed.

What to buy?

Try not to buy cultivars. Instead, get a plant that is as close to the native plant as possible. To do this, make sure the botanical/latin name from books is the same as the one you are buying.

LAVENDER
Lavandula
angustifolia

CHAMOMILE
Matricaria
chamomilla

ROSE
Rosa

ONION
Allium
cepa

GARLIC
Allium
sativum

THYME
Thymus vulgaris

MARIGOLD
Calendula
officinalis

28

Our seven best starter herbs

These are useful and easy herbs to help start your herb garden. With these herbs you can cover many ailments.

Calendula *(Calendula officinalis)*

Easy to grow from seed, hardy annual, likes the sun. Pick the flower heads and it can flower for nearly 11 months of the year. Can grow in pots.

Uses: anti-inflammatory, heals skin, antimicrobial. We infuse it in oil to make a skin healing oil that we add to HWBB ointments.

Chamomile *(Matricaria recutita)*

Easy to grow from seed, prefers well drained soil and sun. Known as the physicians' plant as it will help other ailing plants growing near it. Can grow in pots.

Uses: great for stress, sleep, calms digestion, soothes inflamed skin.

Thyme *(Thymus vulgaris)*

Well-drained soil in full sun. Cut back after flowering to stop it getting straggly.

Useful for colds, coughs and fever. We always put it in our cough medicines.

Lavender (*Lavandula angustifolia***)**

An evergreen perennial shrub that likes full sun and poor, gritty soil. Great for putting in pots, inside or outside or in small spaces. Harvest the flowers from mid summer when the oils have had a chance to develop and the flowers are fully open. Prune the plant heavily after flowering, but stop just short of cutting into the old wood. Lavender has a wonderful calming effect on the nervous system, can help promote sleep, soothe headaches and relax muscles.

Uses: you can dry it and include it in tea mixes (but not too much as it can be bitter), or make a tincture, or use dried lavender for its scent.

Onions *(Allium cepa)*

You can grow onions from seed, but the more common way of doing it, which is easier and quicker, is to grow them from sets (small onions). Plant sets in autumn or spring, 10-15cm apart in well-prepared moisture-retentive fertile soil in full sun. Keep the area weed free and water in dry periods. Harvest the onions when they're big enough to eat or the leaves have turned brown and started to wither.

Uses: Onion is a great antimicrobial herb for coughs and colds. We use it in our fire cider.

Garlic *(Allium sativum)*

Divide a bulb of garlic into cloves. Plant in October/November in a sunny well drained and well nourished spot. Push the cloves well down into the soil so that only the tip is showing. They are ready when the leaves start to brown and wither around June/July. Lift and continue drying out in a dark well aerated space. Best tied up in bunches for 3 to 4 weeks.

Used for coughs and cold. You can grow Garlic in a container.

Rose *(Rosa damascena or Rosa gallica)*

Choose a suitable spot - if they are tall climbers, support is needed. With bush types consider how big they will get. Dig a large hole, fill the bottom with compost or well rotted manure from a safe source: Put some earth on top of that, carefully spread the roots out pruning any that are damaged, and place so that the root collar is just above surface level. Backfill the hole firming around the stem. If you haven't put any compost in the hole give it some liquid Rose Feed and water well. They need little maintenance apart from water, but hate competition, so mulch around to deter unwanted plants invading.

Uses: any fragrant Rose can be used. Harvest petals for calming, soothing teas or glycerites. Harvest the rosehips for immunity.

Make a pollinator garden

Pollinating insects are on the decline as a result of loss of habitat, climate change, use of pesticides and insect diseases. Gardens are vital reserves of habitat for insects. If you create a pollinator garden you will be supporting vulnerable species, and you will benefit from better harvests and healthier plants.

Pollinators - different species of bees, hoverflies, beetles, flies, butterflies and moths - need three main things to thrive: pollen, nectar and shelter. The key to maintaining a good population of pollinators within your garden is to plan for a succession of flowers throughout the year so that they always have access to these essential things. Include a range of shrubs and trees as well if you can.

Spring: Hawthorn, fruit blossom (Apples, Currants, Cherries and Plums), Catmint, Hyssop, Sage (can follow through until autumn)

Summer: Yarrow, Vervain, Lavender, Lemon Balm, Honeysuckle, Passionflower, Mallow, Oregano, Angelica, Borage, Nettles, Valerian, Wild Strawberry

Late Summer/Autumn: Goldenrod, Echinacea, Common Ivy, Bugle

Winter/Early Spring: Barberry, Oregon Grape, Witchhazel, Rosemary, Primrose, Willow.

A personal observation from the HWBB medicine garden*

I have been noticing the many pollinators that are in the garden. The solitary bumble and honey bees love herbs, particularly the mints and any purple lipped flowers. The Hyssop, Oregano and Lavender get covered in them, as do the very tiny flowers of the Figwort.

Ants will harvest blackfly by massaging them, drinking the clear milk produced and often moving them to their nests by cutting off their wings and carrying them there. I watched a Sage bush over a period of a week as it was invaded by blackfly. Then came the ants and completely cleared the blackfly from the plant, leaving the bush quite healthy! I don't destroy ants nests willingly. Ladybirds of all denominations will eat greenfly. Their larva is easy to spot, as it is a large grey

---

* *Josephine Slater, HWBB*

bug, sometimes with yellow stripes. Lacewings will also eat greenfly. Ground beetles of all sorts are good, but beware of the beautiful iridescent purple striped rosemary beetle about the size of the little finger nail, which will decimate any Rosemary and occasionally Lavender and Sage. Squash it quickly! Earwigs will eat aphids and help keep fruit trees healthy. All bugs, bees, butterflies, moths and hoverflies will help and encourage birds into your patch.

RHS research has shown that 27 million gardeners in Great Britain care for an area bigger than all the Nature Reserves put together. This puts us all in a place of great responsibility towards our small bit of the world.

The health benefits of gardening

There are so many health benefits to getting out there amongst the plants and soil in the garden all year round. Studies consistently show that gardening provides benefits for mental health and physical health with stress reduction, assisting with social interaction as well as providing healthy fresh seasonal food to eat and herbs to drink or cook with.

The boost to vitamin D levels from being outside in the sunshine are proven to help our immune systems. Even though we can't get vitamin D from the sun between October and March in the UK, it's still worth getting out into the sunlight for the impact on our serotonin levels, which helps in regulating the sleep/wake cycle and improving mental health.

Gardening involves physical exercise, and as long as we don't injure ourselves carrying heavy loads it is all beneficial for cardiovascular health.

Interacting with the soil enables us to take onboard healthy soil bacteria that can improve health, as well as simply being around all plants and inhaling their oils in the form of chemicals called phytoncides. Phytoncides have antibacterial and antifungal qualities which help plants fight disease and when people breathe in these chemicals, our bodies respond by increasing the number and activity of a type of white blood cells in the immune system, lowering our blood pressure and reducing stress hormone levels.

The human mind responds positively to things like the varying shades of green seen in plants and also to fractal patterns, such as those found in the veining of leaves or the crossing of branches, and to natural garden sounds like birdsong. It's worth getting into the garden or taking a walk amongst the wild plants at all times of year whatever the weather.

Herb growing tips from herb gardeners

We asked some well known herb growers to give us their three best tips. Their responses highlight how diverse and varied gardening is...

Helen Kearney, Elder Farm

Herbs move around, they don't stay where they are planted and there is nothing as strong as a self seeded plant! If a herb appears somewhere new, try and make space for it to grow there, it will probably be super strong and healthy. Herbs also seem to appear from nowhere so look out for new things emerging and ID them before weeding!

Growing from seed is much easier than you think and a very cost effective way of getting lots of plants. It's a challenge to see what you can get to grow from seed, even if the growing instructions are complicated, have a go and see what grows.

Save seeds of herbs and trees, it's quite simple to harvest seeds of lots of useful herbs and trees. Look up the specific growing instructions for the seeds you have harvested (some seeds need a cold period to germinate) and go for it. You will end up with lots of baby herbs and trees to plant and give away. Give the baby herbs encouragement, we talk to all the seeds we plant (a custom we started with one of our long term volunteers), tell them how well they are doing when they are growing and play happy dance tunes when working in the field.

Chris Roe, Subtle Apothecary

There are all kinds of books available with specifications for soil types, shade and light preferences and other tips for growing herbs, but more often than not I find that successfully grown herbs seldom conform to any written advice. I have Marshmallow doing well in well drained soil and herbs supposedly doing well in poor soil enjoying rich humus.

There is a myth that herbs do best in poor soil, certainly many herbs thrive in poor soils in the wild but often due to reduced competition. In the garden, given a less competitive environment, they often grow healthier and better in rich soil. I have found that herbs do well in good garden soil with plenty of organic matter. Having good soil also helps with the removal of perennial weeds and general cultivation. I would advise enriching the soil with good well balanced compost. Manure, however, should be reserved for only a few herbs, such as Roses.

Herbs can be hard to grow from seed, so without a well set up propagation space, it's best to buy in plants, many herbs will then self-seed readily once established. Seed that is collected from the space in which it is grown will often grow far more readily, being acclimated to that specific area.

Sarah Weston, The Organic Herb Growing Company

Always save seeds. Organic herb seeds can be hard to come by and saving seed from your already established herb plants means they are acclimated to your site and will thrive.

Cut back all Mediterranean herbs after flowering to encourage new growth from the base and stop the plants from getting too woody: Thyme, Rosemary, Sage, Lavender, Hyssop.

Always just give it a go and try growing something new or a different herb every year.

"Gardener"

Medicine Making

In this section, we talk about some of the different ways that you can prepare the herbs once you have collected them. There are also instructions on how to make the most common types of preparations.

Types of preparations

Internal

Infusions - fresh or dried herb left to brew in hot water for ideally 20 minutes, then strained. Usually flowers or leaves. Essentially a herbal tea.

Decoctions - herb parts that are a bit tougher e.g. berries, bark or roots: simmered in water for around 20 minutes and then strained.

Cold infusion - for herbs with high mucilage content, such as Marshmallow root. (Also great with herbs that are pleasant consumed cold e.g. Cleavers, Mint or Lemon Balm). Herb put in cold water and left overnight, then strained.

Tinctures and fluid extracts - alcohol extraction (long shelf life, but not suitable for those who avoid alcohol). Tinctures can be made with fresh or dried plant material. Herbs are macerated for a few weeks in a mixture of alcohol and water and then strained. Tinctures are very commonly used in herbal medicine. Spirits like vodka or brandy can be used.

Juices - e.g. for Cleavers and fruits, this is a great way to consume Sea Buckthorn. Can be frozen to preserve.

Syrups - sugar or honey added to a decoction. Improves palatability, sugar preserves in high concentrations. If you add alcohol, it's called an elixir.

Glycerite - herb steeped in glycerine and water. Glycerine is sticky and very sweet. Suitable for diabetics.

Aromatic waters - distilled herbs and water. After distillation you end up with a solution of volatile oils in water, lovely for digestive issues.

Herbal vinegar - herbs infused in vinegar, usually apple cider vinegar. Great for extracting minerals.

Oxymel - a herbal vinegar with added honey.

External

Infused oils - can be made with a dried or semi dried herb in a bain-marie of oil, such as Almond oil. Or can be made in a jar in the sun.

Ointments - oil with beeswax or carnauba wax (vegan) melted together in a bain-marie, to make a semi- solid consistency. The oil can be previously infused with herbs.

Plasters - ointment spread onto cotton or lint.

Poultices - direct application of herb material to skin/body.

Compress - cloth soaked in liquid herb extraction (infusion or tincture e.g.) and applied to body.

Liniment - infused oil and tincture mixed.

Creams and lotions - water and oil-soluble ingredients mixed together (so require an emulsifier).

Medicine making

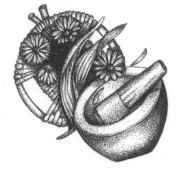

These are detailed instructions on how to make some of our most useful herbal preparations. There are more specific recipes throughout the book.

One of the most important parts of medicine making is sterilising bottles to stop things from going off, and having some muslin handy, perfect for straining everything through. Bottles and jars can be sterilised by putting them washed (not dry) into an oven at 160°C for 10 minutes, or you can use a dishwasher.

A crucial and sometimes overlooked part of medicine making is to label what you have made with the name of the product, the ingredients and the date. There is nothing more frustrating than random bottles of things that you cannot remember what they are!

Always store your herbal medicines somewhere safe, out of reach of children and preferably in a cool dry place, out of direct sunlight.

How to make some medicines

Herbal infusion and decoction

(see Herbal preparations, page 40)

Herbal vinegar

These are a great way of preserving herbs and an easy way to incorporate herbs into your daily life. Many of the medicines in the herb cart are vinegars like our fire cider and mineral rich vinegar. We use unpasteurised apple cider vinegar as it is a probiotic full of useful enzymes and bacteria. Vinegar taken before food has a big effect on balancing blood sugar levels.

Chop the herb finely and cover with unpasteurised apple cider vinegar.

You can use herbal vinegars by taking 1-2 teaspoonfuls a day diluted in water, or use in salad dressings or other types of cooking.

Oxymel

An oxymel is a traditional way of taking herbs that combines vinegar with honey. We use 3 parts unpasteurised apple cider vinegar with 1 part raw local honey - both good for supporting immunity.

Chop up your herbs as finely as possible and then fully cover with vinegar. Leave for 3-4 weeks. Strain through muslin. Mix in the honey.

Take 1-2 teaspoonfuls a day in a little water, can also be used on salad dressings or on veggies.

Tincture

Tinctures are very commonly used in herbal medicine. They are a water and alcohol extract, extracting more constituents out of the plant than just a tea, and it lasts for longer too. Spirits like vodka or brandy can be used.

Chop your herb as finely as possible to expose as much surface area as possible. Cover in vodka and leave for 4 weeks.

Strain and decant into sterilised bottles. Store in a cool, dark place. Dosage is tricky as it depends on why you are using it and what works for you. Different herbalists have different opinions about dosage ranging from a few drops of tincture to 15-20 ml daily. Often we use a blend of different tinctures mixed together and the dosage would be 2-3 teaspoons of the tincture in a little water. For prevention, it could be 5 ml (5ml = 1 teaspoon) 1-2 x a day. Start with 1 teaspoon, see how it is and then increase if you need to.

Glycerite

Glycerites are a great way of making herbal extracts that are not alcohol based, and it is an excellent preservative. Palatable for children as they are sweet tasting. Our cough medicine and 'stress relief' medicine in the herbal cart are available as glycerites or syrups.

Buy food-grade vegetable glycerin. The ratio of liquid that covers the herb is 70% glycerine and 30% water. This is because the glycerin on its own isn't good at pulling everything out of the plant, the water helps with that.

Chop the herb finely and cover in the mix of glycerine and water.

The glycerite needs heat to get a good extraction. Leave for 4 weeks in the sunshine. If you are doing this in the winter, you can put the mix in a heat proof jar and put in a pan of hot water for several hours on a low heat, or use a ceramic based slow cooker. Strain and decant into sterilised bottles.

Syrup

A herbal syrup is prepared by combining a concentrated infusion or decoction with either honey or sugar. If you are making a syrup from an aerial part of a herb make an infusion. If you are making a syrup from a root, bark or berry, then make a decoction. You then mix the infusion or the decoction with honey or sugar to help thicken and preserve it. They also sweeten the mix which then tastes nice and is soothing, useful for sore throats, coughs and digestive issues. One of the most popular herbal syrups is Elderberry syrup, which makes an excellent immune tonic for the winter. We give out cough/immune support syrup in the project.

To make the syrup use a ratio of 2 parts infusion or decoction to 1 part sugar. So if you have 100ml of infusion/decoction then use 50g of sugar. Simmer until the sugar is melted and then bottle the syrup into sterilised bottles while the syrup is still hot. If you put the lid on straight away it will create a seal and hopefully keep the syrup from going off. Store in a cool dark place and once opened, keep in the fridge.

Balm

A balm is a combination of wax and infused oil, melted together, sometimes with essential oils added in at the end.

45 ml oil: e.g. almond, olive, sesame etc. We use olive oil as it is easy to buy and nice for the skin. The oil can also be pre-infused with a dried herb.

3.5-4.5 g beeswax

14 drops total of calming essential oil(s) of choice

Over low heat, warm the oil in a double-boiler or bain-marie. Add the beeswax, warming until just melted. Remove the double-boiler from the heat. Add the essential oils, stir, and then swiftly pour into tins before the mixture hardens. Allow to cool before putting the lids on as condensation can cause moisture to be trapped inside.

January

January can feel quiet after the festivities of December. This is a good time of year for us to take care of our energy. It is a time to incubate ideas for the coming year and decide what seeds to plant in the months ahead. By now, most of the leaves are on the ground, apart from the evergreens still standing tall and proud. The plants have died back and have become dormant. Underground roots are storing nutrients ready for the next growing season. The trees are bare of their leaves and the month has a stark beauty. We can take a lesson from this incubating time and spend some time being still, snuggled up with a medicinal broth or a delicious Turkey Tail chai.

Herbs for harvesting

Wild:

Dandelion root

Horseradish root

Yellow Dock root

Pine needles

Holly leaf

Ivy leaf

Medicinal Mushrooms:

Birch Polypore

Turkey Tail

Oyster

Oyster mushroom

Winter weather, the dark early nights, and viruses make this time of year testing for our immune systems. We've put together some recipes that will help to support you through the coming month.

Mushrooms

Herbs such as mushrooms and seaweeds support the immune system to function optimally, making them invaluable winter allies. Every mushroom contains immuno-modulating polysaccharides, beta glucans and chitin, which are embedded in the cell walls. These polysaccharides contribute to the anti-allergenic, anti-infective, anti-tumour, and systemic anti-inflammatory effects seen in studies. Some of the most renowned medicinal mushrooms that are good to eat include Shiitake, Porcini, Oyster mushrooms, Lion's Mane and Maitake. But you could use button or chestnut mushrooms too.

Oyster mushrooms are probably the most simple medicinal mushroom to grow and they help lower cholesterol, are protective of the liver, are anti-bacterial, and are full of antioxidants.

For more information on mushrooms have a look at:
Mushrooms and Other Fungi in Great Britain & Europe, by Roger Phillips
Medicinal mushrooms, by Martin Powell

Mushroom and Seaweed Immune Stock

Mushrooms need to be cooked for at least an hour to release these immune properties. The best way to do this is in stews, soups or stocks.

Make a stock of a variety of mushrooms, seaweeds, and warming culinary herbs which support circulation, such as Thyme, Oregano and Rosemary. Put the stock on a low heat or in a ceramic based slow cooker and simmer for several hours. Once cooled you use straight away or add to ice cube trays and use a few every time you cook. You can also add a bit of hot water and drink it as a broth.

Turkey tail

Turkey Tail Chai Syrup

Turkey Tail has an ancient history of being used as a medicinal mushroom in many parts of Asia, but is also a very common fungus to find in the UK. It is used to optimise immune function, strengthen the lungs and improve resilience.

Ingredients:
125g dried Turkey Tail mushrooms
10g cloves
50g green cardamom pods
10g allspice berries
20g black cardamom pods
30g whole black peppercorns
25g star anise
3 cinnamon quills
3 decaf tea bags
A thumb sized piece of fresh ginger - grated
A thumb sized piece of fresh orange peel
500g sugar
750ml water

Blitz Turkey Tail mushrooms in a blender, add to slow cooker with water and leave on a low setting for 4-8 hrs.
Prepare spices: put cardamom, cloves, pepper and star anise in pestle and mortar and crush. Break up cinnamon quills and add to a pan with the rest of the spices and dry fry for a few minutes (be careful not to let it burn).
Add orange and ginger to the Turkey Tail mix in the slow cooker and leave to infuse for 2 hrs.
Transfer into a pan and add the sugar, bring to boil and then reduce heat and simmer for an hour until thickened.
When nearly done, rip open the teabags and pour tea leaf into the syrup.
Allow syrup to cool a little then strain through muslin and bottle.
You should have around 500ml syrup. Will last up to 4 weeks in an airtight jar.

To enjoy: add 25/30ml of syrup to a cup of milk of your choice and warm.

Leona Wilkinson from St. Werburghs Farm Cafe, Bristol

Iranian Pickled Garlic

Garlic is a great anti-microbial so very useful at this time of year for all the viruses being passed around. This recipe includes raw Garlic, which is the best way to take it for fighting off colds.

¼ of each of these ingredients, diced: cucumber, carrot, celery, aubergine, cauliflower or broccoli and one green bean

Peel a whole bulb of Garlic (separate into cloves) and one shallot. Leave whole

2 whole red or green chillies

2 tbsp turmeric powder

1 tbsp Angelica or Nigella seeds

1 tbsp flax seed

1 tbsp coriander seed

1 tbsp thyme

1 tbsp ginger powder

1 tsp salt

Put all the above in a glass jar and mix.
Boil enough apple cider vinegar to cover, let it go cold and pour over the veg. Make sure there is no air in the jar before sealing.

Leave for 2 weeks before using.

Zohreh, Bristol

Garlic

Gardening tips

January is a quiet month in the gardening calendar.
Time to contemplate your garden and assess the coming year.

Seeds/planting

Now is the time to check seed packets and throw away any that are
out of date. Time to order seeds of annuals or perennials you haven't
already gathered. Visit local gardening clubs or allotment seed swaps
and see what you can find.

Garden maintenance

This is also a time to assess your garden or plot. Are there areas that
need to be changed or improved? While things are quiet you can also
finish pruning trees and roses. Clear any paths of dead and rotting
foliage, giving any decking or paved paths a good scrub with a hard
brush to remove slime.

Make sure your tools are in good shape. Oil and sharpen any that
need it. Inspect seed trays and pots: wash clean of fungus and debris.
Tidy your shed and drink hot wine!

Wildlife

Be careful when moving heaps of leftover weeds, old rotting stalks,
and piles of sticks if you are tidying up, as there may be a hedgehog or
hibernating insects there that need the shelter until the frost danger
has passed in your area. Break ice on ponds, put dishes of water out
for the birds to drink and bathe, keep bird feeders clean and topped
up with a high protein food to see them through to the nesting season.

February

The first of February is the Celtic feast of Imbolc, marking the point at which life begins its spring cycle. Even though plenty of wintry weather may still be on its way, and the year's lowest temperatures could yet be reached, we can start to see signs of life. This may be in the form of buds on trees, flowers like snowdrops, early daffodils and the bright yellow lesser celandine. Early shoots of Cleavers are young and tender at this time of year so can be used for tea, but since they are yet to become stringy or develop their sticky hairs, they can also be eaten or juiced.

Conifer trees like Spruces, Pines and Firs can be used for their tips or their resin. Any members of these three conifer families can be used medicinally.

Herbs to harvest this month

Wild:

Pine, Spruce and Fir needles
Young Chickweed aerial parts
Young Cleavers aerial parts

Medicinal Mushrooms:

Turkey Tail

Spruce

Conifer Medicine

Spruce (*Picea* species), Pine (*Pinus* species), or Fir (*Abies* species)

In February and March look out for the fresh needles, one of the very early signs of spring - bursting in bright green clumps from the ends of the branches. These vibrant tips make a fresh tasting tea infusion, high in vitamin C. The strong volatile oils are good for low immunity and chest infections at this time of year.

Early French and British colonialists in North America drank this tea to stave off scurvy. Introduced to the remedy by the indigenous people, it ultimately aided the westerner's survival in those early harsh times. The course of history may have run completely differently if those first colonisers weren't so generously helped.

Conifer Resin-Infused Oil

(Spruce, Fir or Pine trees only - don't misidentify with Yew!)

To collect the resin, take a knife and look for places in the conifer trunk where the tree has been damaged in the past, and you will see a sticky oozing white or clear substance that smells strongly. Flake this sticky resin into a clean jar, taking care not to damage the tree.

The cone is the seed-bearing part of a conifer tree, which drops to the ground, opening when the conditions are just right to release the seeds. They often collect resin from the tree before they fall, which forms white strongly-scented crystals. Look for cones on the ground that may also have resin deposits on them and include them in the jar.

The resin will be sticky and hard to clean so it is easiest to wash your knife with alcohol.

Fill the jar with olive oil and leave it for several weeks in a warm place to infuse, shaking it regularly. The resin will dissolve into the oil leaving it strongly scented. Strain any bits out and use the oil to rub on tired achy joints and muscles.

Conifer Tip Tea

A herbal tea or infusion can be used with any fresh or dried plant.

Take 1 approximate teaspoon of the fresh needles and cover with hot water.
Leave for at least 15-20 minutes.
Drink 1 to 2 cups a day.

Conifer tips can be brewed into beer with molasses added for extra nutritional value. You can use the tips from any species of spruce, pine, or fir tree for tea or for brewing beer.
The resin is antibacterial and excellent for healing wounds. You can gather it from the main trunk of the tree where it's secreted to heal injuries on the tree.

Cleavers

Cleavers *(Galium aperine)*

Cleavers, otherwise known as sticky willy because of the sticky hairs that make it cling to you, is a great traditional spring tonic. Often used as a juice or cold infusion to help cleanse the body after the winter.

Topically, it is a cooling, soothing anti-inflammatory remedy for dry, cracked, hot, irritated skin, or for bites.

Cleavers-Infused Oil

Chop a handful of fresh Cleavers, put in a bowl and cover with approx. 300ml of sunflower or olive oil.
Place the bowl over a pan of hot water, cover and leave to infuse on a low heat for a couple of hours, making sure the water doesn't boil dry.
Strain and repeat the process with more chopped fresh cleavers, using the already green oil and re-infuse for a couple more hours.
Strain and leave in a bowl or jug overnight to allow for watery fluids to sink to the bottom and pour off the infused oil into a sterilised bottle and label.

To make into a **Cooling Cleavers Lotion** for hot, irritated skin:

Put the 200ml of cleavers oil back into the bowl, add 20g of beeswax (or 30g of canuba wax if vegan) and reheat until the wax melts.

Take off the heat and leave to cool. When it's almost cool, but not solid, add about 200g of pure aloe vera gel and 20-30 drops of Lavender essential oil and mix well.

Pour in sterilised jars and label.

Edwina Hodkinson Bsc (Hons) NIMH from the Anti-fracking Herbal Clinics

Gardening tips

Planting

Some seeds can now be sown in a cold frame or inside. These include Basil, Parsley, Thyme, Wild Strawberry and Cowslip. Outdoors you can sow German Chamomile. Parsley seeds respond well to being soaked overnight in hot water, they have a very hard shell and germinate better this way. The Blackcurrants planted in autumn need to be pruned by half, leaving a bowl shape. Check the buds and if they are swollen, pick them off, as they may have the 'Blackcurrant big bug mite' which can reduce the fruiting ability.

Garden maintenance

Repair and maintain any paths in your garden: cleaning any paved paths with a stiff brush, replenishing any wood chip paths, and cutting grass paths towards the end of the month. Be aware of any hibernating wildlife.

If you are making a new path, you might consider covering it with cardboard. It works provided the cardboard is thick, there are no gaps, and the wood chip is at least 2 inches thick on top! When the weather is dry start hoeing any unwanted weeds. There's no point working the soil if it's cold, frosty or very wet. Prepare new ground for planting if possible.

Wildlife

Continue to feed the birds a high protein diet to keep them in good shape for the breeding season.

March

It's the third month of the year, and the gardeners are itching to get outside.

Signs of life in the hedgerows, maybe a Coltsfoot on the sheltered side of a sand dune is shining bright yellow. The odd Daisy and Lesser Celandine, the Daffodils and Primroses are usually in full bloom with the rising temperatures. Tree sap rising, time to tap the Birch. Time to use spring tonic herbs like Cleavers and Dandelions, to get everything moving in the body after the winter months.

Herbs to harvest this month

Cleavers aerial parts

Chickweed aerial parts

Cramp/Guelder Rose bark

Cherry bark

Dandelion leaf

Nettle leaf (before flowering)

Violets aerial parts

Willow bark

Spring Tonic Vinegar

(or Mineral Vinegar)

This is a medicine that we give out as a cleansing tonic and to help people to get vital minerals in their diets. It contains herbs that can help with allergies such as hay fever and can be used as a hair rinse for thinning hair.

Pick all the mineral rich spring herbs that help with elimination in the body. Herbs could include: Chickweed, Dandelion root, Dandelion leaf, Nettle leaf, Cleavers, Plantain and Yellow dock root.

Chop finely and cover with unpasteurised apple cider vinegar.

You can use herbal vinegars by taking 1-2 teaspoonfuls a day, or use in salad dressings or other types of cooking.

Dandelion *(Taraxacum officinale)*

Dandelion signifies nature's power to burst through the cracks in our industrialised world, demonstrated by its ability to thrive in the most urban of settings. It grows across Europe and Asia, familiar to millions and many have loved it since childhood, playing the game of blowing the seeds and making a wish. It reaches out and spreads its medicinal properties. We advocate honouring the Dandelion in your garden, by "harvesting not weeding".

Dandelion is a bitter herb with an action on the liver and kidneys. In March, leaves are harvested and used fresh as tea or in salads as a digestive, diuretic and cleansing remedy. The root, when harvested in spring, is especially bitter and useful for people who need to cool an inflamed liver from too much winter excess of fatty foods and alcohol. The roots are more traditionally harvested in autumn, when the long tap root has stored nutrients for the winter, giving a sweeter building and nourishing medicine.

Horta Vrasta

A Greek recipe, meaning "boiled greens" traditionally made with Dandelion - a tasty side dish.

About 100g of Dandelion leaves
1/4 cup extra virgin olive oil
Sea salt and lemon juice

Trim any roots off the greens and rinse very well.
Fill a large pan with water and bring to a boil. Add the dandelion, a pinch of salt and simmer until the stems are soft and tender: between 10-20 minutes, depending on the thickness of the stems. Drain.

Dress with the olive oil, lemon juice, and salt to taste.

Dandelion

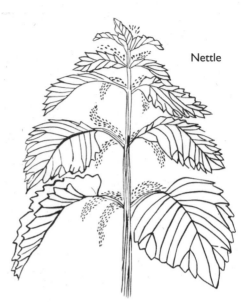

Nettle

Nettle *(Urtica dioica)*

Nettle is the herb that as herbalists we most often turn to when someone is feeling weak and needs help to build strength. It is famous for its mineral content, particularly iron. You only have to look at it to see its power, as it reaches for the sky on its long stem, bristling with prickly hairs, ready to defend itself. Nettle has been in Britain for a long time. It was growing here before the last two ice ages, but only really took hold alongside human settlements. Nettle has always been an ally plant to us. Used as food, to make cord and textiles, and of course as a herbal medicine.

Famously, the Romans are credited with bringing Nettle seeds with them to Britain and used the nettles to beat themselves with to keep warm. Some people maintain this practice, known as "urtication", as a counter-irritant and to bring blood flow to joints to help treat arthritis. Nettle is the perfect embodiment of a spring tonic that activates you after a sluggish winter. But fear not, you can just drink it as tea or eat it, no need to beat yourself with it!

In March, the Nettle leaves will be perfect for picking (wear gloves and take a pair of scissors and a paper bag to drop the Nettles into). Nettle leaves should be gathered in spring rather than summer. When

Nettle starts making flowers, it will start producing cystoliths - microscopic rods of calcium carbonate - which can be absorbed by the body where they may interfere with kidney function. Come early autumn there will be a fresh flush of new Nettles that you can gather again. Dry the leaves for tea, or make a mineral vinegar by infusing in cider vinegar. Nettle will keep you strong all year long.

Samanta's Nettle Pie

This recipe is from Albania. We met Samanta at Project Mama. It's a family recipe that's been shared through the generations.

Plenty of foraged Nettle tops
2 large eggs
Large spring onions
Feta cheese
Olive oil
Plain flour with a pinch of salt
Water
Seasoning

Give the Nettles a wash after harvesting, pat dry then chop them up and put them in a bowl. Chop up the spring onions and add to the Nettles.
Add the eggs and plenty of seasoning along with a good amount of feta cheese, which should be crumbled before adding.
Drizzle with olive oil and leave.

Next, make the pastry by adding small amounts of water to the flour until it makes a dough.
Coat the oven dish in olive oil and preheat the oven to 180°C.
Flatten half of the pastry into the dish to make a thin layer, and then add the Nettle mixture on top.
Then use the remaining pastry for the top layer.
Brush the top with olive oil so it's nice and golden when cooked.

(Check after 30 minutes to see if it's cooked - it might need a bit longer.
NB: Eggs can be replaced with tofu and feta cheese with vegan cheese.)

Birch *(Betula alba)*

The Birch is a potent medicinal tree. The bark and leaves are anti-inflammatory and are very useful to promote detoxification of the body through the liver and kidneys, helping with bladder and skin complaints. The sap is very nutritious and full of natural sugars, amino acids, enzymes, vitamins and minerals.

Birch Sap Tapping Recipe

The best time to tap is in the first two weeks in March nearest the full moon, (depending on region).

Choose Birch, Sycamore, Field Maple, Lime or Walnut (there are 80 different plants you can use sap from).
The size of the tree should be at least 25 cm across, look for a big crown at the top and a tree on a south facing slope if possible. Use some brewing pipe about 10mm in diameter and use a 9mm or 10mm drill bit. Either use a battery powered drill or a brace and bit.

Choose the south-facing side of the trunk and find a flattish part about 45 - 60cm up from the ground. Use a 5-litre water bottle and drill a hole in top of the lid to feed the pipe through.

Cut the pipe to have enough length to reach the hole you make in the tree and go into the bottle lid. Drill/bore a hole at a slight angle upwards so the sap runs down easier. Keep the drill bit steady and straight when going in. Go in about 2 or 3 cm then withdraw, wait a second or two and it should flow/bleed.

Insert the tube, have a small knife handy to cut the pipe down slightly if necessary. If it stops running, get down there and suck the bottle end of the pipe. Place the bottle on flat ground, use string around the tree or sticks in the ground to prop the bottle.

Check in a day or two, don't take more than 5 litres from one tree and use the sap within a day or two as it will go cloudy and ferment.
To plug, whittle a dead branch, ram in and snap off or use potters clay to fill.

Drink, brew, freeze or boil down to syrup (you need approximately 120 litres to make 1 litre of syrup for Birch.)

Enjoy your wild vegan super drink.

Birch Sap Wine

4.5 litres fresh Birch sap (not cloudy)
2 organic lemons
1 sweet orange
1kg of organic raw sugar
Normal wine yeast

Sterilise & rinse all equipment thoroughly.
Add sugar to 1.5 litres of sap & heat gently until dissolved.
Don't allow to boil as it will kill off minerals. Stir frequently. Peel
lemons and oranges. Add to the sugar mixture. Heat until they
dissolve. Save aside the lemons & oranges. Put the 1.5 litre Birch
sugar syrup into a 5 to 10 litre food grade plastic bucket with
the rest of the cold sap. Squeeze the lemons and oranges into it.

Check temperature. When at 20°C, sprinkle yeast on top. Don't
stir. Don't add yeast if above 20°C as it might kill it. Seal lid of
bucket with air lock half-filled with water. Keep a constant
temperature of 20°C, using an electric heat-belt or wrap in
wool blankets. The airlock should start bubbling after a day or
two.

After 2-4 weeks, use muslin to strain off the peels and fill a
demijohn. Top up with spring water to the neck of the demijohn,
if needed, to make sure there's minimum oxygen inside.
Place cork with an airlock half full of water. Ensure temperature
is between 16°C and 21°C. Leave for over a year.

Before bottling, check the specific gravity with the hydrometer
to see if fermentation is complete. Or taste it and if it's still
sweet, something isn't right. Bottle with recycled sterilised
bottles. I use waxed corks.

Storage temperature for wines is 10°C to 13°C.

Birch

Gardening tips

Planting

Annuals like Calendula, German Chamomile, Californian poppy, Nasturtium can be sown outdoors if the weather is warm and the ground workable.

Biennials such as Angelica, Mullein and Perennials such as Echinacea, Yarrow, Hyssop, Lovage, Agrimony, Vervain, Hops, Skullcap, Wood Betony, St John's Wort can also be planted in the seedbed or trays for planting out from early summer through to autumn. If it's very cold, cover the seed trays with glass to give some warmth. Water seeds and new plants regularly.

Divide Mint, Lemon Balm, Hyssop, Lady's Mantle, Elecampane and any other perennials that look congested, then replant to increase your stock and to give away. Watch out for late frosts and cover any emerging delicate seedlings or shoots of perennials that are exposed with fleece or newspaper, straw or bracken if a frost seems likely.

Garden maintenance

Carefully clear debris away from plants, watching for the overwintered ladybirds and other friendly insects. Trim back old stalks and damaged parts. Start to prepare beds for planting, making the soil as fine and crumbly as you can.

Wildlife

The overwintering insects will still need protection. Amphibians will be heading back to their ancestral ponds to lay their eggs. You can put food out at night for hedgehogs who will be coming out of hibernation, removing leftovers in the morning. Feed the birds.

April

We can really feel the days starting to grow in length now that we are past the point of equal day and equal night at Spring Equinox. Everything is properly waking up; it seems like every day it's hard to keep up with all the new signs of spring. Buds are bursting into flower on the trees and at ground level we see herbs such as Primroses, Sweet Violets and Wild Garlic carpeting the woodland floor.

This time really feels like we can start to throw off the shackles of winter constriction. In times past herbalists would have described the herbs we use now as herbs to clear away the phlegmatic winter humours. If you can, go for a walk and mindfully gather a handful of herbs to make a pot of tea with on your return - Nettle, Cleavers and white Deadnettle make a tasty, shining green brew.

Herbs to harvest this month

Wild:

Birch leaf

Blackcurrant leaf buds

Coltsfoot flower

Chickweed aerial parts

Cleavers aerial parts

Dandelion leaf

Daisy flower

Ground Ivy leaf & flower

Lungwort leaf

Nettle leaf (before flowering)

Plantain leaf

Speedwell aerial parts

Violets aerial parts

White Deadnettle leaf & flower

Wild garlic flower & leaf

Cultivated:

Cowslip flower & leaf

Primrose flower & leaf

Plantain

Plantain *(Plantago spp)*

Plantain is one of our favourite herbs as it is so easy to find and it has so many uses. You are not far from either Ribwort or Greater Plantain in the UK, which can be used interchangeably. It is known as 'nature's natural plaster' as it can be used to stop bleeding and it heals burns and wounds on the skin. Used as a lung tonic, it also helps with allergies.

Plantain can be used in lots of ways. You can make an infused oil for all the topical applications, a tincture, a vinegar or oxymel (see instructions in intro on how to prepare herbs in these different ways) or a simple herbal infusion, covering a small handful of the herb in hot water for 20 minutes.

Plantain Poultice

Another wonderful way to use Plantain to draw infections from the body is a fresh poultice. This can be used to treat insect bites or stings, splinters, boils and skin infections.

Method
Take some fresh plantain and mash it up in your mouth.
Apply the mashed up plantain to the affected area or splinter. This poultice will reduce the inflammation and eliminate any itching as it dries.

Use whatever you have lying around to hold on the plantain, either gauze and bandages, any kind of tape or plaster. For a splinter you need to keep it on overnight, and then soak the skin in warm water.

Reapply plantain if needed, to bring the deepest embedded splinters right out.

For Nettle stings, you can either make the poultice or rub the leaves until green juice flows and rub it all directly on the sting.

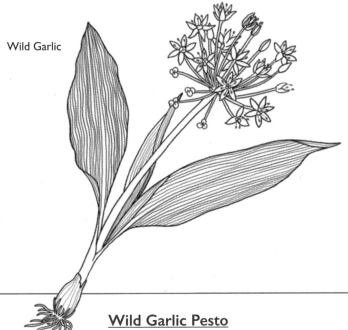

Wild Garlic

<u>Wild Garlic Pesto</u>

This is a delicious adaptation of a pesto recipe, but instead of using basil leaves you use fresh Wild Garlic leaves.

150g fresh leaves (you can add the flowers)
50g pine nuts or cashew nuts
50g parmesan or 30g nutritional yeast
150ml olive oil
1 chopped garlic clove

Salt and pepper to taste

Whizz up all the Wild Garlic leaves, parmesan or nutritional yeast, Garlic, lemon zest and pine nuts to a rough paste in any type of food blender. Slowly add the oil to make the final paste.

This can be used with pasta or as a condiment for any type of meal! It's lovely with roast veggies.

Pickled Ramson (Wild Garlic) Buds

Start by picking your Ramson flower buds. Some people prefer buds that are firmly closed, some prefer them when they have started to open and you can see a couple of flowers peeking out- so gather a selection of both, avoiding those that are fully open as these can fall apart when pickled.

For each small (200ml) jar you will need:

50ml water
50ml vinegar (cider or white wine vinegar)
3 tbsp sugar
½ tsp salt
Optional – a bay leaf or a handful of pepper corns

Slowly heat the water and vinegar.
Add sugar and salt, stirring till dissolved, then bring to the boil.
Allow to cool.

Place Ramson buds and optional extras (if using) in sterilised jars and pour over liquid.
Seal jar and leave for a couple of weeks.

Daisy-Infused Oil

Fill a jar with Daisy flowers, cover with olive oil.

Leave in the sun to infuse for 3 weeks before straining out the flowers.

The old name for Daisy was 'bruisewort', so it is our native equivalent of Arnica.

This can be used for all bruises and bumps.

Daisy

Muscle Rub

Possibly our most popular medicine that we give out. People find it hugely relieving for joint pain, old injuries and stiff muscles. Many people come back month on month just to get a top up.

80ml Comfrey-infused olive oil
10g cocoa or shea butter
10g beeswax
Essential oils of Birch (30 drops) ginger (10 drops) Wintergreen (25 drops) Lavender (15 drops) and Rosemary (20 drops)

Makes 2 x 50ml jars

Directions:
Place the infused oil, cocoa butter and beeswax in heatproof bowl over a pan of gently simmering water (a bain-marie or double boiler).

Once everything has melted, remove from the heat, add in the essential oils, mix well and then pour into sterilised jars.
Leave the lids off the jars until the balm has cooled.

Muscle Rub testimonial:

"…Two months ago, I got full pain in my back, so I can't do anything… So I remember I had this. I use it 3-5 times a day and when I finish after 3 days, I feel really better and thank you…" Ashan

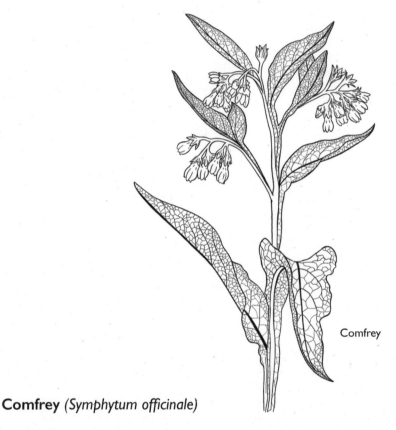

Comfrey

Comfrey *(Symphytum officinale)*

Comfrey has dual use: a herbal remedy and a garden fertiliser.

For medicine, we use *symphytum officinale* (common comfrey) which has variable coloured flowers that can be cream, mauve, pink, purple or white.

For accurate ID, check how the leaf attaches to the stem in a book. It heals joints, skin and bones, fracture, sprains and arthritis, giving it the folk name 'Knitbone'.

Comfrey-infused oil is part of the joint and muscle balm that we give out. It is one of our most popular medicines. It contains constituents which may lead to liver disease for certain people, so to be safe, do not use it in pregnancy or breastfeeding or for more than six weeks. Avoid comfrey root internally.

Gardeners use Russian comfrey (*S. uplandicum*), especially its cultivar Bocking 14. You shouldn't use Russian comfrey internally (it's ok externally) but it's excellent to use as mulch or fertiliser. A liquid comfrey fertiliser is richer in minerals than farm manure.

Comfrey Liquid Fertiliser (stink-free!)

1) Harvest leaves from April. Insert a large terracotta pot with a drainage hole inside a larger plastic pot that has no holes. The terracotta pot should fit snugly inside the plastic, with at least 2 inches space underneath.

2) Tear and crush the leaves & pack tightly into the terracotta pot, to the brim. Most comfrey fertiliser recipes will tell you to add water at this stage, but that will give you a putrid end result. The leaves will rot down by themselves without water, giving you a more concentrated and healthful fertiliser.

3) Put a lid on the container to keep out rain. Leave for 2-3 months or longer if it's cold. When most of the comfrey has disappeared and the plastic pot is full of thick brown liquid, it's done.
4) Drain off the liquid. Store in a bottle.

To use, dilute 1:20 fertiliser to water.

Gardening tips

Planting

Sow annuals directly outdoors e.g. Parsley, Calendula. Continue sow-ing the perennials and biennials mentioned in March, such as Marsh-mallow, Ladies Mantle for planting out late summer/autumn. Softwood cuttings, like Rosemary, Thyme, Passionflower, Lavender, Honeysuckle are ideally taken now. Check the RHS (Royal Horticultural Society) website as it has clear information on how to take cuttings. Never let the cuttings dry out. Check for damaged stems on aromatics, and lightly prune to promote bushy shape. Plant climbers that are ready to go out - like Hops, Passionflower, Honeysuckle - against a fence or wall and provide support as they will grow very tall.

Garden maintenance

Keep on top of unwanted weeds, looking out for plants that are just beginning to appear, such as St John's Wort and Skullcap. Weed out the prolific Valerian which can self seed everywhere and become a nuisance. It will grow well in a large pot and the roots are then much easier to harvest.

May

When May arrives, it feels like the world is alive again, full of beauty and promise. The Hawthorn blossom, also known as the Mayflower, is in full bloom and carries with it a magic of its own. The branches of this tree would be used as decoration for the Celtic festival of Beltane, to celebrate good health and sexual vitality. The vibrant red Clover starts to appear in the meadows, along with many other plants. Towards the end of the month, the bitter sweet scent of the much loved Elderflower bloom is in the warmer air. You never have to look far to find the umbrella like clusters of tiny Elderflowers.

Herbs to harvest this month

Wild:

Comfrey leaf

Chickweed leaf & flower

Cleavers aerial parts

Dandelion leaf

Daisy flower

Ground Ivy leaf & flower

Hawthorn leaf & flower

Nettle leaf

Plantain leaf

Speedwell aerial parts

Raspberry leaf

Red Clover flower

Rose petals

Shepherd's Purse leaf & flower

White Dead Nettle leaf & flower

Violets aerial parts

Pine pollen

Cultivated:

Calendula flower

Californian poppy aerial parts

Lemon balm leaf

Seaweeds:

Bladderwrack

Carrageen Moss

Dulse

Kelp

Lava

Elderflower *(Sambucus nigra)*

Elderflower

Dubbed 'the medicine chest of the country people', the Elder tree has been associated with many folk tales of good and bad luck, medicine and witchcraft. The associations with bad luck and witchcraft perhaps stem from attempts by the church to break people's pagan relationships with nature. In pre-christian times it was a symbol of good luck to plant an Elder close to the house, and the reverence of this tree still persists in Europe today. Planting it in your garden really does mean that you have a medicine chest on your doorstep.

Use the scented flowers as a tea to dry up excessive nasal secretions. Useful when you have a cold, but also for allergic conditions such as hay fever. Can be used for fevers during a viral illness. Rather than suppressing the fever - an important part of the immune system's response to illness - we support the body to move through it by using diaphoretic herbs like Elder, inducing sweating to break the fever. If you have a fever of over 39 degrees for three or more days then contact your GP.

The berries make a wonderful antiviral immune tonic, and the leaves can be used externally as an insect repellant. The bark has an emetic effect and has been used in the past to expel parasites.

Elderflower Champagne

Dissolve 700g of unrefined sugar into 3.5 litres of hot water, then add 2.5 litres of cold water.
Leave to cool.

Add 15-20 heads of fresh Elderflowers, 2 organic lemons chopped and zested. Don't wash the Elderflowers. They are covered in wild yeasts so you do not need to add any.

Cover with muslin and leave for 3 days.
Check the mix - if it is not starting to fizz, add some yeast.
Leave for another 3 days, then strain and bottle.
The champagne can make lots of gas so you need to check and let off gas every few days.

This fermented drink will have lots of bacteria which can help with replenishing gut flora and an assortment of digestive problems as well as have the properties of Elderflower which can help with allergies, excessive catarrh and fevers.

Cold and Flu Tea

One of the herbal teas that we give out frequently throughout autumn and winter.

Equal parts of dried:
Elderflowers
Peppermint leaves
Yarrow leaves and flowers

Take a palm-sized amount of the mix and steep in a teapot large enough for three mugs. Leave for at least 20 mins and then drink hot (adding more hot water if it's cooled down).

Drink 4 cups a day during a fever. You can also soak a flannel in lukewarm tea to put on the forehead or wrap around the feet.

Hawthorn flowers and berries *(Crataegus spp)*

Hawthorn is the archetypal medicine for the heart – both physiologically and emotionally. It is a member of the Rose – Rosaceae – family and is found abundantly in hedgerows, fields, woods, and parks throughout the British Isles. Traditionally blossoming around Beltane at the beginning of May, it is known as the May Tree and has typically been the chosen material for May Day garlands.

Hawthorn is harvested in spring for its young leaves and flowers, and in autumn for its red berries. It has a protective presence and is the pagan symbol of fertility and resilience. However, despite these positive associations, it has been considered bad luck to bring Hawthorn into the home for fears it invites illness and death!

Traditional herbalism knew Hawthorn as a heart tonic, and now modern pharmacology has corroborated its benefits for both the heart and circulation. Hawthorn berries are rich in flavonoids and procyanidins, which dilate the coronary arteries to strengthen the heart muscle's contraction – while relaxing the blood vessels, so as not to increase heart rate or raise blood pressure. In this way it is said to have a 'normalising' effect on the heart health.

We use Hawthorn flowers in our Relax Tonic and the berries in our Rejuvenating Tonic and Children's Immune Syrup. While there are suggestions that Hawthorn can be used for a range of heart conditions, always consult a physician when considering hawthorn for any diagnosed heart conditions – it can interact with other medications.

Hawthorn Oxymel

An oxymel is a traditional way of taking herbs that is a combination of vinegar with honey.

We use 3 parts unpasteurised apple cider vinegar with one part raw local honey - both good for supporting immunity.

Take a cup full of Hawthorn flowers, leaves or berries and cover with vinegar.
Mix in the honey.
Add a pinch of Rose petals if desired.

Take 1-2 teaspoonfuls a day in a little water.

Hawthorn is our native heart medicine. It can physically support heart function and the integrity of the blood vessels.

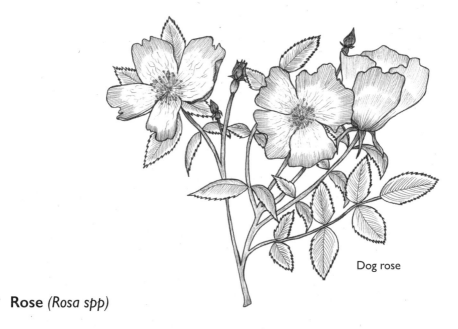

Dog rose

Rose *(Rosa spp)*

Rose petals are used as medicine all over the world for their uplifting scent. Rose is said to be able to heal broken hearts, and is specific for grief and loss. We use wild Roses as well as any cultivated Rose that has a scent. Rose is also an anti-inflammatory and an astringent.

We have heard many tales of using Roses from people we have met at the refugee support projects around Bristol. Bushra from the Yemen says that they use the Rosewater for flavouring sweets and also use it as face masks for the skin and the lips, they also drink rosewater medicinally for the urinary tract and for strengthening the heart.

Kurda from Iran, co-ordinator at Refugee Women of Bristol, says that they used to tie a string though the rosebuds and hang them around clothes for the scent. Several Iranian people have described the incredible festival of Rose and Rose Water that is held in Kashan, Iran every year during the second half of May.

Rose Cold-infused Water

Rosewater is usually made by distilling water and Rose petals together to make a hydrosol, or floral water. It is possible to do this at home using kitchen equipment, but for a simple easy alternative, you can start by using the method below:

Gather as many deeply scented rose petals as you can find and cover with distilled water.

Cover and leave this to infuse for 24 hours and then strain. It keeps for 2-3 days or longer in the fridge. You can add alcohol to preserve for longer.

Use the rose-scented water as a spray, to drink or to use on your skin.

Medicinal Seaweeds

Seaweeds have been harvested from our shores for millennia and have been used both as food and medicine. They are highly nutritious, full of protein and fibre, various different minerals and the vitamins A, B, C and E.

Seaweeds, which are a type of algae, contain lots of different chemical constituents to help them survive such harsh conditions like being in the sun all day, submersion in salt water and the bashing of the waves. Some of these constituents are potent antivirals, they support our immune system as anti-inflammatories and help our bodies be more vigilant to abnormal cell growth.

They also can help balance thyroid function due to their iodine con- tent. Some brown seaweeds like Kelp contain a lot of iodine that can exacerbate high thyroid function so be careful if you have hyperthyroidism or an autoimmune thyroid problem. Consult your local medical herbalist if you want more advice on taking seaweed. In coastal areas of Ireland, Wales and Scotland when people were coming down with a cold, they would harvest some fresh seaweed and boil it up like a broth to eat.

Some of our favourite seaweeds are Dulse, Kelp, Pepper Dulse, Sea Spaghetti and Serrated Wrack. You can dry, then add to stocks and stews (see Mushroom and Seaweed Immune Stock in the January chapter) or powder them and add to meals. Just like mushrooms, the cooking process is important for releasing the medicinal compounds.

They are an important source of food and shelter to a variety of sea life. They also act as a carbon sink, helping keep the levels of carbon dioxide manageable and ameliorating some of the effects of climate change. This means it's very important to be as sustainable as possible whilst gathering seaweed: harvest only what you need, never pull it off the rocks but trim the top third from the frond with scissors instead, don't take any animals that are attached, rotate harvesting spots.

For safety, only harvest seaweed that is still attached to a rock. Check if the sea is clean at: *https://environment.data.gov.uk/bwq/profiles.*

For more information on identifying and harvesting seaweeds along with recipes, visit Prannie Rhatigan at *www.irishseaweedkitchen.ie* or *www.gallowaywildfoods.com/an-introduction-to-seaweed-foraging.*

Kelp

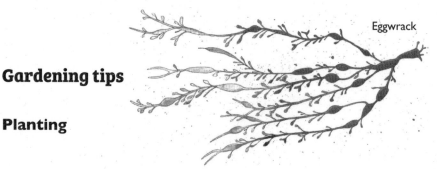

Eggwrack

Gardening tips

Planting

This is the end of the busy spring sowing season. Thin out seedlings, giving plants a chance to grow. Seedlings will need constant attention, moving to a semi-shady spot if the weather is too warm. Pot them on if you have the time. Keep checking for slugs, and check for blackcurrant fat bugs.

Garden maintenance

Start a new compost heap and distribute the old one where it's needed.

There are differing opinions as to how much a herb needs to struggle to produce the best medicine. The most natural habitat you can create for any given herb is best, i.e. Mediterranean herbs like south-facing,, fairly poor soil, but Comfrey likes a damp semi-shaded spot with a bit of compost. Sort any herbs in containers, taking off the top two or three inches of soil and replacing with new; repotting where the plant is too big.

If you have tender herbs such as a Lemon Verbena inside, put them out on a tray to catch the runoff from watering.

Wildlife

Keep feeding the birds. Create a log pile for sheltering beetles and centipedes. Leave the Dandelions for pollinators.

June

June marks the peak of summer and culminates with the longest day of the year, the summer solstice, falling on the 21st or 22nd. But it is Midsummer's Night when it feels most potent to go out into nature or into the garden. Solstice means standing still, and it almost feels that on this night that the garden is holding its breath, waiting for the longest day. On this night, protective herbs are traditionally thrown into the solstice bonfire: St John's Wort, Mugwort, Marigold, Vervain and Yarrow.

On the morning of the longest day, the dew formed on the leaves of Lady's Mantle is said to have magical properties of transformation. We use Lady's Mantle in our Women's' Tonic Tea. This tea helps with heavy, painful or irregular periods and helps mothers heal after birth.

June is a bumper time for herb gathering with so many herbs ready to gather. You will see that this chapter is bursting with herbs!

Herbs to harvest this month

Wild:

Chamomile flower

Comfrey leaf

Daisy flower

Ground Ivy leaf & flower

Elder flower

Horsetail stem & branches

Honeysuckle leaf & flower

Herb Bennett root

Lady's Mantle leaf

Ox-Eye Daisy flower

Plantain leaf

Pellitory-of-the-wall aerial parts

Raspberry leaf

Red Clover flower

Rose petals

Skullcap leaf & flower

Self-Heal leaf & flower

Shepherd's Purse leaf & flower

St John's Wort aerial parts

Speedwell aerial parts

Vervain aerial parts

Wild Lettuce aerial parts

Wild and Water Mint leaf
Wild Oregano leaf & flower
Yarrow

Cultivated:

Globe Artichoke leaf
Borage leaf & flower
Blackcurrant
Calendula flower
Fennel leaf
Feverfew aerial parts
Hyssop flower & leaf
Lemon Balm leaf
Mint leaf

Seaweeds:

Bladderwrack
Carrageen Moss
Dulse
Kelp
Lava

Mugwort

Soothing Solstice Tonic

Lemon balm and St John's Wort Tincture
(Melissa officinalis and Hypericum perforatum)

Solstice is a great time to harvest these herbs, which are both thriving at the height of the summer. St John's Wort normally flowers around the 24th June so we believe harvesting at this time captures the energy of the solstice to use all year round.

We like using this combination of St John's Wort and Lemon balm to help lift the spirits and ward off the winter blues, but it's also anti-viral, especially for the cold sore virus, and so helps when you're feeling run down. If you make it as a tincture you can save it to take in the winter when you may be really needing some of that summer solstice energy.

Method
Chop up the leaves of Lemon Balm and the leaves and flowers of St John's Wort as finely as possible.
Cover in vodka and leave for 4 weeks.
Strain, bottle and label.

Dose 1-2 teaspoons a day diluted in a little water.

When not to use this:
St. John's Wort can accelerate the liver's processing of drugs so shouldn't be used with medication that needs to remain constant like the contraceptive pill, blood thinners and immunosuppressants.

Do not use Lemon Balm on a daily basis if you have an underactive thyroid.

Lemon balm and St. John's Wort

Calendula - also known as **Marigold** (*Calendula officinalis*)

Commonly called Pot Marigold - named after the pot that it was cooked in, as it used to be commonly added to soups and stews. Marigold originated in Egypt and was brought to the UK by the Romans and has been widely cultivated since the 12th century. The name may come from the dedication to the Virgin Mary in the Middle Ages, 'Mary's Gold'. If you dreamed of Marigold, it was a portent of good things to come!

Marigold is widely used in Arabic and Indian cultures, in cooking and as a colourant, also medicinally and in cosmetics. The petals make a great addition to a salad as do the very young leaves.

It is a real bringer of light, reflecting the healing warmth of the sun's rays into the body, collecting on a warm day is one of the great pleasures, the sticky resin seeping from the sepals reminds us of the power to close and mend wounds, sticking together soul and body. As the sun goes down, the petals close for the night, reminding us to rest.

Calendula is an anti-inflammatory, anti-microbial "vulnerary" herb - which means it is a healer of tissue. Externally, it is taken for any inflammation of the skin, ulcers, minor scalds and burns, and internally as an anti-inflammatory for the digestive tract for any kind of indigestion. It has the reputation of helping delayed and painful periods and vaginal thrush. The resin of the plant is anti-fungal.

Infused Calendula Oil

Harvest your flowers - make sure you pick some that are bright and fresh.

Once picked, it's best to allow them to dry out for a day or two (so that there is slightly less water content and lower risk of the oil going off).

Fill a sterilised jar with the flower heads and top up with an oil of your choice. We use olive oil as it is easy to get hold of and great for the skin. Other options are almond, sesame or hemp seed oil.

Seal your jar and place in a warm spot for 2 weeks. This could be a sunny windowsill or on a radiator.

For a faster option, infuse the oil by using a double boiler or bain-marie. Place the herbs and oil in a heatproof bowl over a pan of gently simmering water for 4 hours.

Strain the oil with a clean sieve or muslin into a sterilised jar. Don't squeeze the herb too much when straining, as it is best to get as little water content as possible in the final oil. This can be kept as an oil or used to make balms or creams.

Because of the risk of bacteria in the oil, it is best not to consume oils infused with fresh herbs – we recommend that they are used topically only.

Calendula

Healing Balm

10g beeswax
10g shea butter
80ml infused Calendula oil (see above)
20 drops Lavender essential oil (1 ml)
20 drops of preservative

Melt the beeswax in a bain-marie over simmering water.
Add in the calendula oil.

Take off the heat and add the Lavender essential oil and the preservative.
Make sure it is completely runny and mixed well.
Pour into sterilised jars.

Leave the tops off the jars until the balm is cooled.

Testimonial for Healing Balm

Thank you so much for visiting Refugee Women of Bristol regularly with your faithful help and kind support. I have been using the Healing Balm, Cold and flu herbal tea, and Blood sugar balance tea freely given by you. They have helped treat my various ailments. I am still amazed at how these natural ingredients work wonderfully and pleasantly on me. I'm sure my GP is happy too that I'm not adding more pressure on top of their crazy workload! I'm truly grateful for what you do to help people!
May the gracious Lord bless you all!

Blackcurrant *(Ribes nigrum)*

Widely grown for its fruit, but little known as a valuable herb. The fruits are beneficial as a health tonic, high in immune supporting flavonoids and vitamin C.

The berries are less well known as being valuable for long-term respiratory infections. Herbalists are hearing tales of people craving blackcurrant juice during Coronavirus infections - a sign that people perhaps intuitively know what they need to recover.

The leaves and leaf buds are also used in herbal medicine as a tonic to help the body recover from periods of prolonged stress or trauma.

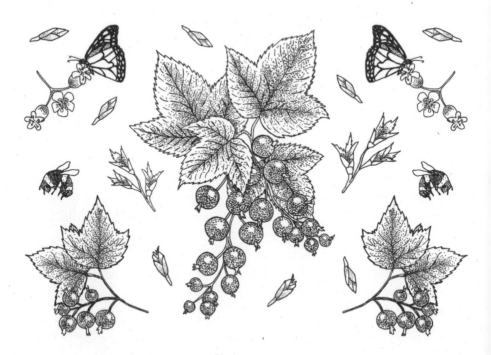

Blackcurrant

Blackcurrant Oxymel

An oxymel is a herb that has been infused in cider vinegar, strained and then mixed with honey. You get the added medicine of the cider vinegar: digestive, anti-inflammatory and antiseptic. Great for coughs and colds.

Rinse berries, remove stalks.
Pack into a large jar and squash them with a masher.
Add a cinnamon stick and pour in enough vinegar to cover.
Seal, shake and store in a cool dark cupboard for 2 weeks.
Strain through a jelly bag/muslin lined sieve, squeeze to get out all the juice.

Measure the liquid and add the same amount of honey or molasses (VE).

Heat gently to dissolve, skimming off any scum that floats to the top.

Pour into sterilised bottles and cap while hot.
To drink, prepare as you would a cordial and dilute with a little hot water.

Store in a cool dark place. Once opened, keep in the fridge and use within 2 months.

It will keep for up to a year unopened.

Gardening tips

Planting

Pot-on last year's plants that need it. Plant out others in their permanent positions.

Climbers such as Honeysuckle and Passion Flower will need extra support for new growth.

Only water plants if they really need it; once you start to water you will have to continue as watering encourages the roots to reach up to the surface for the drink. It is better for the roots to go down to stay cool and moist naturally.

Soak a thirsty plant occasionally rather than sprinkling often, and do this in the evening so evaporation is limited.

Calendula are very accommodating and will grow almost anywhere but prefer a light free draining soil in full sun, they will self-seed and are easy to propagate from saved seed. If they like their home, you will find they appear all over the place in late spring.

Although technically an annual, they will survive the winter in a sheltered position. Good at deterring asparagus beetle and tomato hornworms. They may develop powdery mildew in early autumn, pick and destroy the affected leaves to prevent spread of the disease.

Garden maintenance

Keep weeds down on paths and beds. Best thing we bought for the herb garden is a light strimmer.

Harvesting

Harvesting will be in full flow: Mint, Lemon Balm, Skullcap, Ladies Mantle, Rose petals, Comfrey leaves, Honeysuckle. There will be a second growth for a later harvest.

The yellow flowers of St John's Wort are traditionally picked on the 24th, the saint's day. Keep picking Calendula flowers to keep them flowering until the frost. Calendula is best picked when fully in flower, midday is best when the dew has evaporated.

Dry in the shade in an airy place. The heads take a long time to dry as they are dense, the quicker you can dry them the more colour will be retained. Keep picking and more flowers will come.

Wildlife

Put out a dish of water with pebbles or stones in the bottom, creating a watering place for pollinating insects and birds. Ground beetles of all sorts are good, but beware the beautiful iridescent purple striped rosemary beetle, which will decimate Rosemary, Lavender and Sage. Squash it quickly!

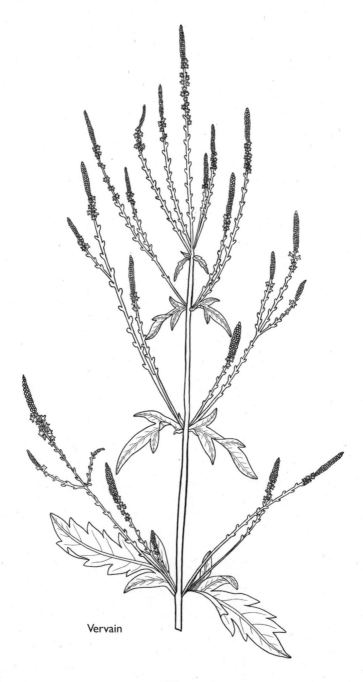

Vervain

July

July brings warmer days, almost everything is growing in abundance and it's a busy time for harvesting.

Scents of Honeysuckle, Rose, Lavender and more permeate the air, flowers open and pollinators are busy. Fruits are swelling and the green canopy of leaves provides dappled shade. We are energised by spending more time outside and enjoy the celebration of nature.

Herbs to harvest this month

Wild:

Alexanders seed

Agrimony leaf & flower

Bilberry leaf & berries

Gypsywort aerial parts

Eyebright aerial parts

Figwort aerial parts

Honeysuckle flower & leaf

Hollyhock flower

Lime/Linden flower

Meadowsweet leaf & flower

Mallow leaf

Mullein leaf & flower

Mugwort aerial parts

Passionflower leaf & flower

Pellitory-of-the-wall aerial parts

Red Poppy aerial parts

St John's Wort leaf & flower

Vervain aerial parts

Wood Betony leaf & flower

Yarrow leaf & flower

Cultivated:

Globe Artichoke leaf

Borage leaf & flower

Calendula flower

Feverfew aerial parts

Lavender leaf & flower

Marshmallow leaf

Motherwort aerial parts

Rosemary leaf

Thyme leaf

Wormwood aerial parts

Milky Oat seed

Passionflower

Passionflower *(Passiflora incarnata or Passiflora caerulea)*

This beautiful trailing flower isn't a native plant but some varieties of it grow readily in our gardens. It needs very little ground space and can be trailed up and over fences and walls, so it's perfect for small gardens, balconies and vertical spaces, preferring a sunny position if possible. We harvest the flowers, and for some species, we add in the leaves and even the stems and tendrils, and dry them for tea or make an alcoholic extract (a tincture).

Used to calm and soothe the heart, Passionflower can really shift us out of our 'fight or flight' mode and into a more restful state. Passion-flower affords us a reason to take a moment and breathe.

It can calm anxiety and heart palpitations and aid restful sleep. It's a vital part of our sleep tea blend, but it doesn't usually make you feel drowsy in the daytime.

A note about Passionflower species:

Passiflora incarnata also called Purple Passionflower or Maypop is the variety most widely used medicinally. You can use the flowers, leaves and stem.

Passiflora caerulea or Blue Passionflower, is often sold in garden centres in the UK as it grows here very well. If this is the type you have, use the flowers only, as the leaves have the potential to be high in compounds related to cyanide that could cause problems if drunk regularly.

Passiflora edulis or Passionfruit Vine is cultivated commercially in tropical and subtropical areas for its sweet, seedy fruit. Can be grown in the UK but needs plenty of sunshine and regular watering.

<u>Passionflower Tincture</u>

Harvest the flowers when fully open, and if you have purple passionflower, also take leaves, stalk and tendrils. It works to cut back the plant but leave plenty to grow and flower next year.

Take a large clean glass jar and chop the fresh plant material very finely, filling the jar to about three quarters full. Only just cover the plant with a clear spirit such as vodka, which is usually around 37% alcohol.

You can weight the plant material down with kitchen weights or a stone to keep it under the liquid or simply shake it frequently.

After 4-6 weeks, strain the liquid off through a clean muslin cloth, squeezing every drop out.

Label it in a clean jar and take a teaspoon a day or in the evening as needed.

Limeflower *(Tilia spp)*

Limeflowers make wonderful relaxing medicine for anxiety, depression and general agitation.

They can be used to promote a deep restful sleep, relieve tension headaches, migraines, stress and high blood pressure.

Very useful if there is tension in the digestive tract like IBS, colic, indigestion or any spasmodic pain like period pain.

The hot tea can be used as an infusion for fevers, especially good for children. It can calm an over-excited child or a child that can't sleep. Cold limeflower tea can be good for hot flushes during menopause.

Linden Blossom Tincture

Chop up your herb as finely as possible, in this case Linden blossom, otherwise known as Limeflower.

You harvest the bright green 'bract' with the flowers, but not the leaves.
Cover in vodka and leave for 4 weeks.
Strain and bottle.

Safe to be used daily, take 1-2 teaspoons of the tincture in a little water.

Honeysuckle Glycerite (sun extraction) _(Lonicera spp)_

Glycerites are a great way of making herbal extracts that are not alcohol based. Palatable for children as they are sweet tasting and also safe for diabetics.

Pick the honeysuckle leaves and flowers, place in a jar and cover in a mixture of vegetable glycerin (food grade) and water. The ratio of liquid that covers the honeysuckle is 70% glycerine and 30% water. Fix the lid on the jar.

Leave for 4 weeks in the sunshine. The glycerite needs heat to get a good extraction. Strain and bottle.

Honeysuckle is a good cold and cough medicine. Use at the beginning of a virus particularly if you have a sore throat.

Use 1-3 teaspoonfuls a day, depending on size of person and severity of cold. Honeysuckle makes a delicious fragrant tea and can also be made into a tincture.

Honeysuckle flowers

<u>Wood Betony Glycerite</u> (heat extraction)
(Stachys betonica)

Wood Betony with its striking purple flowers is often found in meadows and coastal areas. Used as a calming, grounding tonic helpful for anxiety and insomnia, it is traditionally used for all ailments of the head, particularly headaches & migraines.

This recipe is to make a hot glycerine extract.

Chop fresh Wood Betony leaves and flowers and pack into a heat-resistant Kilner jar. Pour straight food grade glycerine over the herbs, poking out all the air bubbles.

Leave about 2 inches of room at the top. Securely clamp the lid. Place the jar in a large pot on the stove and fill the pot part way with cold water.

Bring to a simmer and heat for 4 - 6 hours. Add HOT water as necessary to keep the pot topped up.

Remove jar from heat and cool till you can handle safely. Press, or strain through muslin bottle and label.

Dose 1-3 teaspoonfuls a day.

Lorna Mauney-Brodek from Herbalista Free Clinic and the Dublin Herb Bike (www.herbbus.org & www.herbbus.org/herb-bike)

Wood betony

Digestive tea

We give this tea out frequently in the projects that we visit and people find it useful for some kinds of heartburn, indigestion and IBS.

Fennel seed
Meadowsweet
Lemon Balm
Chamomile
Mint
Calendula

Take equal measures of each herb, cover with hot water and steep for 20 mins.

Meadowsweet is an anti-inflammatory herb and digestive aid. It soothes and protects the mucous membranes of the digestive tract and stomach lining whilst reducing acidity, making it ideal for upset stomachs.

Soothing tea

This is another digestive tea that we give out. It is useful for when people have the burning pain of heartburn or ulcers or any kind of internal inflammation.

Marshmallow root
Plantain
Chamomile
Marshmallow leaf

Cover 1 teaspoonful of herb in a cup of hot water,
Leave for 20 minutes, strain and drink.

Meadowsweet

Gardening tips

Planting

Keep an eye on your newly planted out herbs. Put a dish under pots to conserve water. You can still sow some perennials and annuals which may germinate more quickly in the warmth and be ready to either bring inside in a pot for the winter or stand outside with some protection. Nasturtium, Dill, Coriander and even Basil will grow enough to crop before the light begins to fade.

Harvesting

This is one of the busiest months for harvesting the flowers and leaves of medicinal herbs. Many herbs will be over by the end of this month. The Lemon Balm & Oregano that has not been cut should be humming with bees. If Lavender is ready, cut it to dry for teas and balms.

Garden maintenance

Continue watching for rosemary beetles which may have spread to Lavender and Sage. The ladybirds you have provided habitat for in the winter will deal with the aphids. Trim and harvest Sage and Rosemary to encourage new growth. You may need to water them if it's very dry to prevent stress. Honeysuckle, Passion flower and Hops will continue to need tying and training along whatever support structure you have for them.

Wildlife

If you're feeding the hedgehogs, continue to do this as the babies will be coming out about now. Watch out for sheltering frogs if you are hoeing, they will eat the slugs!

August

August starts with the festival of Lammas or its older name Lughna-sadh on August 1st, a traditional time of the first cut of the harvest, also known as "first fruits". We see the Blackberries beginning to ripen in hedgerows and on wasteland. Canal sides and river sides are a good place to harvest, away from the fumes of the road. If you're lucky enough to know the location of a Mulberry tree, gather these most delicious berries that are nourishing to the body and soul.

Some herbs are still flowering: Honeysuckle permeates the air in cities and countryside alike. Yarrow is in abundance. Mugwort lines the side of roads and footpaths.

This is also the time when a lot of plants are turning to seed and certain herbs are collected when they have seeded, such as Wild Carrot, Nettle and Milk Thistle. The message of this time is to look around and harvest the fruits and seeds of nature's labour, appreciating all the work the plants have put into ensuring their survival.

Herbs to harvest this month

Wild:

Alexanders seed	Lime/Linden flower
Agrimony leaf & flower	Meadowsweet leaf & flower
Bilberry leaf & berries	Mallow leaf
Blackberries	Mullein leaf & flower
Gypsywort aerial parts	Mugwort aerial parts
Eyebright aerial parts	Nettle Seeds
Figwort aerial parts	Passionflower leaf & flower
Honeysuckle flower & leaf	Pellitory-of-the-wall aerial parts
Hollyhock flower	Red Poppy aerial parts

St John's Wort leaf & flower

Vervain aerial parts

Wood Betony leaf & flower

Yarrow leaf & flower

Cultivated:

Globe Artichoke leaf

Borage leaf & flower

Calendula flower

Feverfew aerial parts

Lavender leaf & flower

Marshmallow leaf

Motherwort aerial parts

Rosemary leaf

Thyme leaf

Wormwood aerial parts

Milky Oat seed

Yarrow *(Achillea millefolium)*

Yarrow's distinctive feather-like leaves can be found throughout the year amongst the grass in pastures and parks, but at the height of summer we see it rising in the hedgerows and banks displaying umbrellas of tightly bunched, dainty white flowers from sleek green stems.

Yarrow may be a delicate looking plant, but it has strong, protective qualities. Its Latin name – Achillea millefolium – refers to Achilles, the Greek warrior, who turned to yarrow on the battlefield in the Trojan war to treat the wounds of fellow soldiers. Millefolium signifies the 'thousand leaves' in the feather, which when applied to cuts, have the ability to stop bleeding and possess antimicrobial and antibacterial compounds that clean wounds. Rub or chew a couple of leaves to release the aromatic oil, azulene, and apply to the affected area.

While yarrow is a great first-aid herb in this sense, it has the broader effect of encouraging the flow of blood around the body by dilating blood vessels. It is therefore great for promoting circulation and helping support a fever.

Yarrow is a key ingredient in our Cold and Flu Tea! Because of its ability to support blood flow, it is a useful herb for digestion and for the female reproductive system. See May for the full recipe.

It can even be used to move stagnant blood and bring on menstruation when needed. Avoid during pregnancy since its stimulating effect can induce contractions!

Yarrow

Marshmallow *(Althea officinalis)*

The leaf, root and flower of marshmallow contain sugars called mucilage which have a soothing, demulcent action that can calm hot irritated conditions. Perfect for scratchy throats, tight chests and dry coughs alongside other immune supporting herbs. We use it as a tea or decoction (see the intro for an explanation of the difference) and this extracts the gloopy mucilage. It is also an antiseptic.

As the name suggests, it likes to grow in marshy areas particularly by the coast. It is not common in the wild so it is a great herb to put in the garden. Easy to grow from seed, but as it's tall it needs plenty of space. Flowers from mid-late summer. You can use the common Mallow root (Malva sylvestris) which is prolific in the wild instead of Marshmallow, but it's not quite as gloopy!

> **Marshmallow Cold Infusion** for acid indigestion.
>
> Use for acid indigestion. Also good for coughs and catarrh.
>
> 1 small handful of roots
> 2 cups cold water
> 1–2 tbsp. honey (optional; if using, manuka is the best)
> Makes 2 cups.
> Keeps for 3–4 days in the fridge.
>
> Soak the Marshmallow in the water for 30 minutes. When softened, process in a blender for a few minutes until smooth. Add the honey if using, and let sit for 4 hours. Bottle and keep in the refrigerator.
>
> Take 2 tbsp. 3 times daily until symptoms abate.

Lavender *(Lavandula officinalis)*

Lavender is often associated with old women. This association may have more to it than a memory of the smell of lavender and your grandmother, because this valuable herb shares many of the attributes that the elder women in our families and societies do. It embodies the qualities of calm, strength and practicality.
Most famously, Lavender is known as a calming herb. Used in pillows to soothe a troubled mind, or in our Calm Balm that people rub on their temples to aid sleep. Lavender can help the nervous system drop out of sympathetic activation of "fight or flight" and into the relaxed state of the parasympathetic, to be able to rest and digest.

Lavender is also a strong herb that heals and cleans wounds as an antiseptic, when used as the essential oil. So much so that in world war two, when surgical supplies were scarce and precious, people were asked to grow Lavender in their gardens to supply the field hospitals. A balm with Lavender oil is always going to be a very useful addition to your first-aid kit.

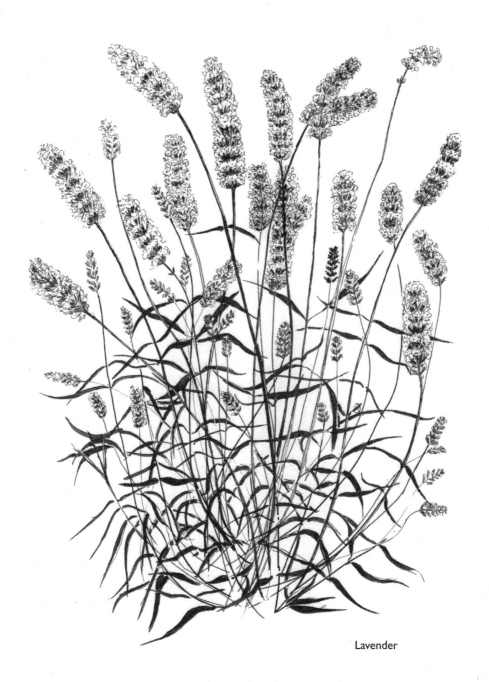

Lavender

Calm Balm

This is a wonderfully strong-smelling balm packed full with Lavender. Perfect for those moments when life feels like it's running away with itself. A little bit of this rubbed into the temples creating a heady aroma Lavender can help calm those nerves.

Makes 2 x 50ml jars

80ml Lavender-infused olive oil
10g cocoa or shea butter
10g beeswax
80 drops of Lavender essential oil

Place the infused oil, cocoa butter and beeswax in heatproof bowl over a pan of gently simmering water (a bain-marie or double boiler). Once everything has melted, remove from the heat, add in the essential oils, mix well and then pour into sterilised pots.

Leave the lids off the pots until the balm has cooled.
Add the Lavender essential oil.
Pour into jars.
Wait until the balms have fully cooled and set on top before putting the lids on.

Sleepy/Relaxing Tea

One of our most popular teas that we give out. Useful for calming daytime anxiety or to aid a more restful sleep at night.

Ingredients: Limeflower, Lavender,
Passion Flower, Chamomile, Oatstraw.

Cover 1 teaspoonful of herb in a cup of hot water, leave for 20 minutes, strain and drink.

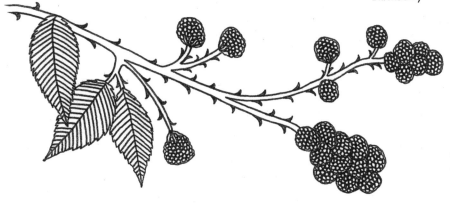

Blackberry

<u>Blackberry Oxymel</u> *(Rubus fruticus)*

Blackberries used to be known as 'gout berry' and were used to prevent gout attacks. Packed full of vitamins and minerals, whilst also being antimicrobial they are useful for colds and sore throats. The berries combine well with Hawthorn to help support blood vessels and prevent heart disease.

An oxymel is a traditional way of taking herbs that combines vinegar with honey. We use 3 parts unpasteurised apple cider vinegar with one part raw local honey - both good for supporting immunity. If you don't want to use honey, just cover it in vinegar.

Take a cup full of Blackberries and cover with vinegar.
Leave for 3-4 weeks.
Strain through muslin.
Mix in the honey.

Take 1-2 teaspoonfuls a day in a little water, can be used on salad dressings or on veggies.

Nettle Seeds *(Urtica dioica)*

Harvest these when the Nettles are heavy with seed, hanging down the stems below the leaves in bright green geometric clusters. Usually ready to pick around the end of July and August through to September depending on the patch, it is easy to confuse small round nettle flowers earlier in the season with the seeds as they are not typically flower-shaped, so wait until you see the flattened deep green clusters.

If they have already turned black, they've gone over. Nettle seeds are adaptogens, which means they help with the general stress response.

They strengthen the kidneys and the adrenal glands. They are packed full of minerals and trace elements just like the Nettle leaves but additionally have omega oils which make them nutritional power-houses.

Dry them and grind with hemp seeds and black pepper as a condiment.

Nettles with seeds

Gardening tips

Planting

Sow some perennials and biennials for planting out next year. Continue to sow biennials such as Mullein and umbellifers such as Angelica, that need a cold start.

To grow lavender well in the UK, it requires alkaline conditions. So put plenty of dolomite or lime into the soil when you prepare to plant a Lavender bush. Also sprinkle it through the topsoil around the plant, forking it in lightly. They like plenty of water and good drainage.

Harvesting

Save some ripe seeds, leaving some for the birds in the winter months (from plants such as Poppies, Calendula, Mullein). Dry them out well on a piece of paper before bagging and labelling. Store in an airtight container.

If you run a community garden, then collecting seeds and putting them in packets to donate is a great way to advertise your garden and get new volunteers.

Calendula will become a nuisance if it likes your soil, so be careful to harvest flowers often and remove unwanted seed heads.

Garden maintenance

Cut back faded Lady's Mantle and Mint to encourage new growth. Outside pot plants, tubs or window boxes will appreciate a "weed and feed". Take off any seed heads, creating some air and light for the plants.

Water well. If you are going away on holiday soak the plot and try to get a neighbour to water for you. If you can, move pots to a shady place to conserve dampness.

Wildlife

Don't forget to top up the bird and pollinating insect water bath. The hoglets (baby hedgehogs) will need to fatten up for hibernation so continue to feed them.

Marshmallow

September

September sees the last days of summer meet the first days of autumn as we cross the equinox of equal day and night into wintertime. This change from light to dark is celebrated at autumn equinox, traditionally the time of the Harvest Festival. It's a time to be thankful for nature's bounty, but also to allow that which no longer serves us to fall away; to let go.

In Old England, September was the Haervest-monath, the harvest month, and September's full moon is still known as the Harvest moon. Now is the time for gathering the ripened fruits of summer as we begin to think about hunkering down for winter. Hedgerows are abundant with berries, including Hawthorns and the last of the bramble harvest.

Stock up with Rosehips, and if you are near the coast, stock up on Sea Buckthorn too, both great sources of vitamin C for winter. Flowers are producing seeds, and leaves are starting to turn. As the first cool nights sweep across, underground mycelial networks start to pop up their fruits too: mushrooms!

Herbs to harvest this month

Wild:

Burdock root (of first-year plant, not yet flowered)

Dandelion root

Elder berries

Hawthorn berries   Rose hips

Hops flower (strobile)   Sea Buckthorn berries

Horse Chestnut seeds (conkers)   Teasel root

Himalayan balsam seed   Yellow Dock root

Nettle seeds   Wild Chicory root

Cultivated:	Medicinal Mushrooms:
Calendula flower	Artist's Bracket
Angelica seed	Birch Polypore
Fennel seed	Cauliflower fungus
Dill seed	Oyster mushrooms
	Turkey Tail
	Ceps

Oyster mushroom

Hops *(Humulus lupulus)*

We collect the strobiles, the female flowers, in late summer/autumn. Hops is used as a sedative to help with sleep, a bitter digestive tonic to stimulate digestion, and is supportive in menopause as it contains plant oestrogens. Especially good for menopausal insomnia.

Hops were extensively grown in the UK for beer making, with vast Hops fields in Kent. Before this a huge range of herbal infused ales were made locally by 'alewives': Wormwood, Yarrow, Juniper, Mugwort, Heather, Ground Ivy (known as alehoof) were all commonly added to beer.

Many herbal remedies were taken in the form of fermented wines and beers, as they were probably safer to drink than the water. In contrast to the sedating Hops these herbs were often psychoactive. The new way of making hop beer was brought over from Belgium in the 16th Century and led to the rise of large commercial breweries. Hops enabled beer to be made more cheaply, efficiently, and in vast quantities.

This history, connecting Hops to beer, enclosures, and the beginnings of market-based capitalism is documented in the excellent pamphlet 'Radical Brewing: Work, energy & Beer' from Bristol Radical History Group.

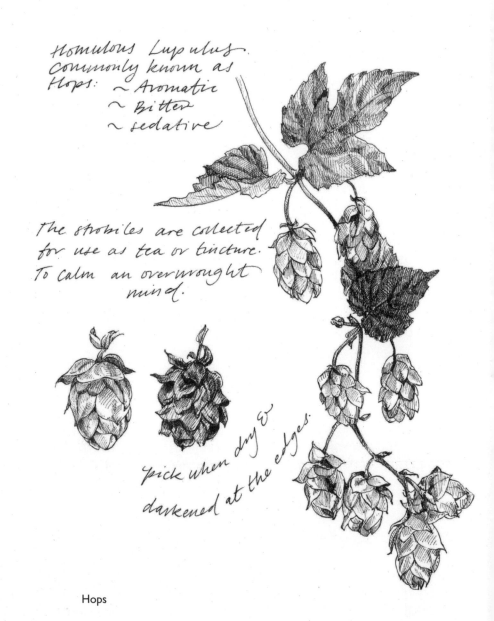

Homulous Lupulus.
Commonly known as
Hops: ~ Aromatic
~ Bitter
~ sedative

The strobiles are collected
for use as tea or tincture.
To calm an overwrought
mind.

pick when dry &
darkened at the edges.

Hops

Hop Pillows

You don't need to drink or eat a herb to feel the effects, smelling them can be just as effective.
Some people experience a strong reaction to herbs when near to them. One person got the best effects from Mugwort for sleep by hanging it above their bed. Sleep pillows are a gentle way of coaxing sleep.

Sew some thin material into a pillow/small bag. Fill it with the dried hop strobiles. Put it near your own pillow for a calm night's sleep. Replenish the herbs every few months.

Medicinal berries

Late summer/early autumn is the time for bumper berry harvests. Berries are such great medicine for a number of reasons.

They contain so many beneficial flavonoids in their skins. These are phytonutrients that protect cells from the effects of ageing and inflammation, protect cardiovascular health and the immune system, as well as being packed full of vitamins and having the best sugar to fibre ratio of any fruit.

Hawthorn berries

Elderberry Syrup _(Sambucus nigra)_

This makes one of our tastiest native immune supporting syrups with Elderberries and any spices you might like to add (e.g. ginger, cloves, star anise). Elderberries are anti-viral, particularly against the flu virus. You can dry the berries, freeze them or make them straight into medicines like syrup or vinegar.

Take as many Elderberries as you have picked, and separate them from the stalks.
Cover in water and boil and simmer for about an hour.
Mash the berries well, strain out the juice and measure the liquid.
Add 1g of sugar or honey to every one ml of liquid.
Stir in the sugar or honey and bring to the boil and simmer for 5 minutes.
Strain and bottle.

The bottles that you use to store the syrup need to be as sterile as possible as the syrup can go moldy easily without this. We often add a splash of alcohol, in the form of brandy, or a tincture to our syrup to ensure it lasts longer.

Take 1-2 tsp a day for prevention and up to 4-5 tsp when ill with winter viruses.

Sea Buckthorn _(Hippophae rhamnoides)_

Sea Buckthorn is a spiny shrub that forms dense thickets on UK coastal sand-dunes and has pale silvery green oval leaves. It is laden with bright vibrant orange berries from late August through September and beyond. This plant is very widespread all over the world, e.g. Europe, Asia, China, Mongolia, Siberia, and often grows in high mountain or desert environments. The berries are adapted to grow in the harshest of places with poor soil, and can help us be resilient to life's stresses. They are very high in vitamins C and E, but also many other minerals and vitamins as well as a wide range of omega oils, flavonoids and antioxidants.

They can help us in so many different ways to recover from chronic stress and we use them in our resilience tonics. They help the immune system, improve our oxygen uptake in all cells in the body, and even protect the liver from damage. They have a delicious sour flavour that you can use in cooking as well as for medicine.

Sea buckthorn

Recovery Tonic Recipe

This is a blend of herbs that build resilience as well as calm the nervous system. We give it out in the projects to help people with long-term stress, insomnia and building immunity.

We use glycerine to make this recipe instead of sugar, so that we know that it is safe to give out to people who are diabetic. But when making this for yourself, you could make it with a sugar syrup.

Add equal parts of the following herbs to a slow cooker:

Rosehips, Hawthorn, Elecampane, Elderberry, Sea Buckthorn, Skullcap, Oatstraw, Nettle leaf and seed. 25-50g of each herb depending on how much you want to make.

Mix together a 70/30 ratio of glycerin and hot water in a jug. Add the liquid to the slow cooker, enough liquid that the herbs have enough room to swim around in.

Set the slow cooker to the lowest setting and leave for about 3-4 hours until the liquid is good and hot but not so hot as you think the herbs are getting crispy.

Then turn it off and allow the herbs to infuse in the liquid overnight. Or if you don't have a slow cooker then use a pan with a lid on, on a very low heat.

The next day, strain through a large sheet of muslin, squeeze to try and get every drop. Bottle the liquid in glass bottles.

It should keep for up to a year outside of the fridge.

Fennel *(Foeniculum vulgare)*

Fennel is a wonderfully uplifting digestive herb that can help with bloating, wind & mood. Seeds are normally used but the leaf is very aromatic too. We often use it as a tea. I teaspoon of seeds, cover in hot water and leave for 20 minutes, often drunk after a meal to help with absorption.

Fennel Seed biscuits

Makes 36, using US measurement cups (about 240ml)
Preheat the oven to 180°C. Line flat baking sheets with non-stick baking paper.

Mix the dry ingredients:
1/2 cup plain flour
1/2 cup porridge oats
2 tbsp ground almonds
1/3 cup dark brown sugar
1/4 tsp baking powder
Pinch of salt, cinnamon, nutmeg
2-3 tsp Fennel seeds (lightly toasted if you like, and crushed)

Mix the wet ingredients:
3 tbsp coconut oil, melted
2 tbsp golden or other syrup
A dash of vanilla extract

Add wet ingredients to dry and mix well.
Drop teaspoons onto the baking sheets, leaving space between; flatten with the back of the spoon or your fingers and bake in batches for 5 minutes.

Leave to cool on the tray for a few minutes, then use a spatula to transfer to a wire rack. Store in an airtight tin (or, eat them all right away).

Pitchfork Cafe (hosting occasional vegan fundraising feasts in and around Bristol)
(www.twotreescatering.org/pitchfork-cafe)

Fennel

Mother's Milk Recipe

We have found that all the herbs that are used for blood sugar balancing are great for stimulating breast milk.

They also are really helpful for colic in a newborn, so if drank by the mama will be passed on through the milk to the babe.

We have two labels for this formula: 'Mother's Milk" and 'Blood Sugar Balancing', with great feedback for both.

Use equal parts of:
Fenugreek seed
Cinnamon bark
Nettle
Fennel seed

For example weigh, 10g of all the above herbs, or whichever you can get hold of, and mix to make a blend.

1tsp of the herbs covered in boiling water, leave for 30 minutes and drink 2-3 cups a day.

Gardening Tips

Planting

Collect seeds and sow hardy annuals, such as Calendula and Californian Poppies, for early flowering next year. Take hardwood cuttings: Thyme, Rosemary and Sage. Take root cuttings of Echinacea and other perennials like Elecampane. A cold frame can protect them over winter.

Divide clumps of perennials such as Lemon Balm, Mint, Ladies Mantle. If old and matted, discard the very old heart. Plant out your spring-sown perennials, such as Marshmallow, in prepared beds. Keep them well watered until the rains come. Cut back Lemon Verbena and dry for a delicious tea. Either bring it in or protect it against the increasingly cooler weather. Take cuttings in case it doesn't make it through winter.

Garden maintenance

Cut back and dry Mediterranean herbs - Thyme, Rosemary, Sage and Lavender - to the base to encourage new growth next year. Sort your leaf and compost bins ready for the leaves and path clearing.

Wildlife

Try not to do an autumn clear-up. Insects, birds and hedgehogs will appreciate piles of sticks, hollow stems etc. for hiding places. Net ponds against the leaves, leaving access for newts & frogs. Remove blanketweed, but leave other plants in the water to provide spring cover for toads to twine their strings of eggs around. Make sure it has stones and sloping sides for easy access.

Autumn flowering Ivy will be humming with bees stocking up for winter.

October

As the days get shorter and there is a coolness in the air, it's time to start wrapping up warm and gathering the final fruits and nuts that the plants have been crafting throughout the summer months. Among the treasures of autumn, we find Rosehips, sloes, sweet chestnuts, and of course plenty of apples!

Feast your eyes on the magnificent changes in colours as the trees start to shed their leaves – Silver Birch in particular puts on a magical display of oranges. As you start to feel the crunch of fallen leaves under your feet, our senses are drawn to ground level: fungi! Further down still, and as the aerial plant begins to fade away, the roots below ground of Marshmallow, Dandelion, Burdock and Yellow Dock are just about ready to dig up.

Herbs to harvest this month

Wild:

Dandelion root

Burdock root

Mullein root

Marshmallow root

Common Mallow root

Solomon's Seal root

Yellow Dock root

Wild Chicory root

Elderberries

Hawthorn berries

Nettle seeds

Rose hips

Sea Buckthorn berries

Cultivated:

Angelica root

Elecampane root

Echinacea root

Milk Thistle seeds

Valerian root

Medicinal Mushrooms:

Artist's Bracket

Birch Polypore

Cauliflower fungus

Hen of the woods

Oyster mushrooms

Turkey Tail

Ceps

Rosehips

Rosehips

Rosehips are a powerhouse of potent plant chemicals including large amounts of vitamin C, which is why people harvested them in WWII when citrus fruits were low. They help enhance immunity, so combine really well with Elderberry and Hawthorn berries. The hips are also beneficial to reduce inflammation, joint pain and balancing blood sugar.

Rosehip vinegar

Collect the Rosehips, cut in half and cover with unpasteurised apple cider vinegar for 4 weeks.

Filter through muslin to catch the itchy hairs and bottle.

This produces a beautiful pink vinegar, to be used daily as an immune supporting medicine, very high in vitamin C.

You can use herbal vinegars by taking 1-2 teaspoonfuls a day, or use in salad dressings or other types of cooking.

Angelica (*Angelica archangelica*)

Believed to be native to Syria, Angelica archangelica has spread to many cool European climates where it has become naturalised, but it isn't as common in the UK as our native form, Angelica sylvestris, which is not as medicinal. Angelica is a wonderful biennial herb to grow because it is a carrot family plant and it can be misidentified in the wild with some poisonous plants. It likes deep moist loam, a shady position, and thrives best in damp soil.

Grow from ripe, fresh seed in late Aug/Sept or propagate from off-shoots. Medicinally, use the stem, root or seeds (see the harvesting advice at the beginning). Considered for centuries to be one of the most important herbs, it has fallen out of common usage and is perhaps only remembered as candied angelica, a treat sold in corner shops. But looking at its properties it is easy to understand why it was so valued in times of rampant disease and poor living conditions. A tonic aromatic herb, it is used as a warming bitter to help with indigestion, wind & bloating, constipation, headaches, colds, coughs and fevers.

<u>Angelica Carmelite water</u>

The original recipe was created by French Carmelites in the 1600's and has been known as an "elixir of life". Since then, there have been many variations

1 bottle of white wine
1 cup/20g fresh lemon balm
1/2 cup\10g fresh Angelica archangelica
Zest of 1 lemon, pinch of freshly grated nutmeg

Put all the ingredients together in a jar and then fill the jar with the bottle of white wine.
Stir well, leave to macerate overnight, then strain.

Enjoy as an aperitif.

Angelica

Dandelion and burdock root cordial

Dandelion and Burdock are traditionally used in combination to support the elimination processes in the body, especially the liver, and to aid digestion.

It's also a combination used to clear the skin.
Originally a fermented mead or beer, this is a simpler, non-alcoholic version of the traditional drink.

Method:
1 tbsp Burdock root
1 tbsp Dandelion root
2cm piece ginger, sliced
1 whole star anise, crushed
1/2 tsp citric acid
200g granulated sugar or honey, or less - to taste

Place all of the ingredients, except for the sugar, with 600 ml of water into a large saucepan and boil for 20 minutes.

Filter the mixture into a serving jug, and whilst the mixture is still hot, stir in the sugar until dissolved.
Leave the mixture to cool.

To serve, add 200ml of tap or sparkly water to every 50ml of syrup in the jug and stir well, then pour over ice.

The syrup should keep for around a week in the fridge.

Dandelion and Burdock

149

Roasted Dandelion Root 'Coffee'

Roasted dandelion root serves as a nutritious and delicious alternative to coffee – great for anyone looking to reduce caffeine intake, but also to reap some of the benefits of one of our favourite but often-neglected 'weeds'!

It's simple to make and you can experiment with taste by adding different spices.

Simply cover a baking tray with Dandelion root and roast at 180°C for 25 minutes – until brown. You can tell when it's ready because the house will start to smell like freshly baked biscuits!

Try adding a sprinkling of Cinnamon, Clove, Cardamom or Fennel.

The drink can be made much like coffee in a cafetière or like tea through a strainer. Add a dessert spoon per cup and let it brew in hot water for five minutes.

For maximum field-to-filter satisfaction, pull out a trowel and dig up your own roots for this recipe! Dandelion roots can be harvested from late autumn through until the end of winter – when the plant is dormant and the plant's goodness is stored below ground.

Come spring, the plant will be shooting up its energy into the leaves and flowers. Once you've dug and cleaned the roots, chop them into 1cm pieces and leave to dry for a few days.

Mushroom harvesting

Mushroom harvesting is a tricky topic when it comes to edible species, as there are a lot of poisonous species to watch out for. There's an old adage that says: "There are old mushroom hunters and there are bold mushroom hunters… but there are no old bold mushroom hunters."

When foraging for medicinal mushrooms it's very possible to stick to safe distinctive species for which there are no poisonous lookalikes, but always confirm your finds by using a good mushroom identification book.

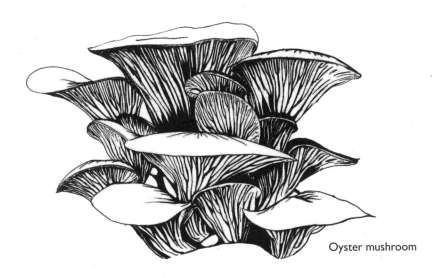

Oyster mushroom

The polypores are a group of mushrooms that grow on dead wood or living trees that don't have gills on their undersides but many tiny pores instead.

Bracket fungi grow like shelves out of tree trunks and the Artist's Bracket, Birch Polypore and Turkey Tail mushrooms are all safe, easy species to start your mushroom harvesting journey with.

Hen of the Woods

Hen of the Woods *(Grifola frondosa)*

This delicious mushroom is also known as "Maitake" which means dancing mushroom in Japanese. The name is meant to have been given after people danced with happiness upon finding it in the wild. It is not rare but it is a big treat when you find one! Often found at the base of deciduous trees like Oak and Chestnut.

They are a sought-after culinary herb with a strong umami taste but also one of our most used medicinal mushrooms. They have a large amount of immune active polysaccharides that are extracted well in water.

These are immune enhancing, anti-tumour, help relieve the effects of cancer treatments and help with insulin sensitivity.

Gardening tips

Harvesting

Roots, Roots, Roots! It's time to dig Marshmallow, Elecampane, Valerian, and wild plants such as Yellow Dock, Dandelion, Burdock (this year's new and soft plants near the mother plant).

Clean and chop them as soon as you dig them up, making them ready to dry. Do this before the weather turns or the leaves die back.

Garden maintenance

Lift and divide big clumps of perennials such as Lemon Balm, Chives, Mint, to replant and give away. Continue mulching and weeding as needed.

Turn the compost and leaves to get air into the middle of the heap. When collecting leaves, check Roses and take off any diseased leaves, especially blackspot, and burn them. Do not compost them as the spores will spread.

If planting Roses, this is the best time to start, from now until January/February when the growth will start.

Wildlife

Clean out and disinfect any bird boxes and build log plies in beds to shelter insects. Put out the clean filled bird feeders.

November

November is the month when the leaves have fallen and the dark nights have settled in. This month starts with what was celebrated as new year's day, coming straight after the celebration of Samhain (the Celtic name for Halloween), the fire festival that marks the beginning of the dark half of the year.

Now is the time for self-care, for noticing that maybe we are more tired and letting ourselves rest when we can and for strengthening our immune system as we go fully into winter.

It may look like there's not much out there to harvest and help us with this, but we need to dig a little deeper.

Now is the time for roots. If you have a space to grow plants, then Echinacea and Elecampane are amazing plants to nurture and now is the time to harvest these to make medicines for your home apothecary, so you are ready for the winter months' coughs and colds. If you are wild foraging, be thankful for the armies of dandelions for its bitter root and keep a beady eye out for some wild horseradish to power you through.

Herbs to harvest this month

Wild:

Burdock root

Dandelion root

Horseradish root

Mullein root

Marshmallow root

Common mallow root

Yellow dock root

Rosehips

Cultivated:

Elecampane root

Echinacea root

Valerian root

Medicinal Mushrooms:

Birch Polypore   Artist's Bracket

Cauliflower fungus   Turkey Tail

Oyster

Echinacea *(Echinacea purpurea)*

Purple coneflower, also known as Echinacea, is such a well-known herb but its origins are often glossed over. A Native American wildflower known to many different Native Americans, including tribes from the Great Plains, Cheyenne, Choctaw, Comanche, Dakota, Meskawaki Fox, Pawnee, Sioux and Omaha, who used it as an antiseptic for wounds and snake bites. Many of the herbs that we use in the UK come from North America, the knowledge of which was shared with the first colonisers.

But was this an equal exchange? Were Native American tribes credited for the medicinal knowledge? Who profited from sharing this stolen knowledge? Do we acknowledge the genocide that occurred when the Americas were first colonised?

One of the ways we can start to decolonise 'western' herbal medicine is by opening up this conversation about the herbs that we use.

Echinacea is a very useful herb for immunity. There are several species, but Echinacea purpurea is the one that grows best in the UK. Grown from seed fairly easily but the slugs love it, so protect the young seedlings!

We use the root and it should be harvested from at least 3-year-old plants. Decoct the root to make a tea or make a tincture (see July) which will help enhance immunity at the beginning of an infection.

Echinacea

Echinacea Throat Spray

for sore throats and tonsillitis
Parts refer to ratios, so it depends on how big your spritzer bottle is.

I part Apple cider vinegar
2 parts cold herbal tea - infused with herbs like Thyme, Sage,
Rosemary, Hyssop
2 parts Echinacea tincture and ½ part Propolis tincture if you
can get it

As soon as you feel your glands are up or your throat feels
sore, spray this directly into the back of the throat 3-4 x daily.

Rooty Cough Syrup

This is one of the cough syrups that we take to the projects. It
is made with the following: Mullein leaf, Marshmallow root,
Elecampane root and you can add Echinacea root and ginger
root. We also add strong antimicrobial herbs like Thyme,
Rosemary and Sage, and warming spices like star anise,
cinnamon and cardamom.

Take equal parts of the roots and other herbs. You can use all of
these or a combination. Chop up the roots & leaves and cover
with twice as much water. Boil and simmer for about an hour.

Strain and measure the liquid.
Add Ig of sugar or honey to one ml of liquid.
Stir in the sugar or honey and bring to the boil and simmer for
5 minutes. Strain and bottle.

The bottles that you use to store the syrup need to be as
sterile as possible as the syrup can go moldy or ferment. You
can add a splash of tincture or alcohol to our syrup to ensure it
lasts longer.

For children take 2-3 tsp a day, and for adults 4-5 tsp.

Chewy Elecampane Throat Lozenges

The root of the beautiful Elecampane is used as medicine to strengthen the lungs and help clear mucus off the chest. It is an expectorant and antimicrobial.

Boil it up in water to drink with ginger, or make into lozenges. You can also make an elecampane glycerite (see July) or an elecampane tincture (See June).

Ingredients
100ml water (or herbal tea)
25g gum arabic
1 tsp honey or glycerine
1 tsp cinnamon
15g ginger
15g Elecampane
4 tsp Marshmallow powder

Finely grate ginger and Elecampane. Heat the 100ml of water, stirring in the gum Arabic until it has melted.

Keep stirring until all the granules of resin have dissolved and simmer until the water has reduced by at least half.
Add and stir in the teaspoon of honey or glycerine.
Stir in the fresh roots, and cinnamon.

Stir in enough mallow powder to create a consistency that is stiff enough to mould. Mould into a ball.

'Flour' a surface and a rolling pin with the remaining mallow and roll the ball into a long thin sausage shape, a centimetre thick. Cut into small lozenge shapes.

You can either leave this out to dry a little, or harden them off in a warming oven if you need them to keep a little longer. Suck freely to soothe sore throats or delicate tummies.

Recipe by Melissa Ronaldson of Herbalists without Borders Calais (www.hwbcalais.org/get-involved)

Elecampane

Gardening tips

Planting

Now is the ideal time to plant bare-rooted Roses (you can also do this in February or March). See the section on planting Roses in the 'Our Seven Best Starter Herbs' at the front of the book.

Garden maintenance

Prune Blackcurrants now if you haven't already. See Gardeners' World website for a good video on how to achieve the classic goblet shape. Pruning can be done on hardwood between now and March, including Apple trees and Roses.

Remove the saucers from pots to stop them from getting water-logged. Wrap up with bubble wrap or old sacks to protect roots and pots against frost damage.

Begin tidying the shed, recycling unwanted plastic pots, getting rid of accumulated rubbish, and sorting out tools. Check for storm damage on trellises, and fences etc.

Wildlife

If lighting bonfires or moving leaves be careful to look for hibernating hedgehogs. Preserve them at all costs as they are beautiful and very useful creatures, vulnerable to extinction through loss of habitat. Keep bird feeders topped up. Clean them regularly to prevent the spread of disease.

December

December brings us the winter solstice: the celebration of the shortest day, and a time to welcome back the light; a rebirth of the sun. In the lead-up to the solstice, the days are short, the nights are long, and yet we can find ourselves busy with deadlines to meet before the end of the year, family to see during the holidays and celebrations to be had. But the darkest coldest days can test us – so bring in the tasty herbal treats at our fingertips. Our fire cider vinegar might be ready to sip and some of our tonics and tinctures will be ready and strained.

Don't forget this month, all the warming culinary herbs that can be added to meals, puddings and boozy drinks - if that's your thing!

This is the time for ginger, nutmeg, chili, cinnamon and cardamom; to keep our hearts warm and our energy strong and carry us into the new year.

Herbs to harvest this month

Wild:

Horseradish root
Holly leaf
Ivy leaf
Pine needles

Medicinal Mushrooms:

Birch Polypore
Oyster
Turkey Tail

Horseradish

Horseradish *(Amoracia rusticana)*

Horseradish is an easy to grow, useful, perennial root that has become naturalised in the UK. It is a cabbage family plant that has been cultivated for hundreds of years and used as a condiment complementing hard to digest fatty meats.

Medicinally, it has a stimulating pungent root that is also antimicrobial and can be used for countering coughs and colds and activating immunity and circulation. The leaves can be cooked as a spicy green.

Fire Cider Vinegar

Inspired by herbalists from the USA, particularly Rosemary Gladstar. This is a warming, immune boosting medicine to be taken throughout the winter to stimulate sluggish circulations and help stave off winter illness. It is very popular when we give it out and formed part of our Immune Pack that we gave out hundreds of during the pandemic.

Take as many pungent herbs and spices as you can (such as, Horseradish root, Turmeric root, chilli, Garlic, Onion, ginger), and some aromatic herbs (such as, Sage or Rosemary).

Chop them up, and add a quartered organic lemon, and a spoonful of honey if you wanted.
Fill a jar and cover with unpasteurised apple cider vinegar.
Leave for 3-4 weeks, then strain.

You can use herbal vinegars by taking 1-2 teaspoonfuls a day. This is quite a pungent herbal vinegar so diluting in some warm water would be recommended.

Holly & Ivy *(Ilex aquifolium & Hedera helix)*

No two plants represent December more than Holly and Ivy. They have been bound together for centuries with references in Christian hymns and symbolism.

But the connection actually predates Christian times. Both are native evergreens used to celebrate midwinter bringing life into the dark homes. Children wore Holly and Ivy at this time of year as a symbol of life's tenacity and re-emergence.

You might not think to grow these herbs in your garden, but Holly was traditionally planted near a house for protection. We now know that Holly leaves act as mini lightning conductors!

Holly and Ivy's nectar, pollen and berries are important food sources for insects & birds in autumn and winter.

Medicinally, Holly leaves were used for fevers as an infusion or decoction and both are used as expectorants to help chesty coughs. The berries are to be avoided as they can make you very sick!

Be careful to wash the ivy leaves as the older leaves have a toxic layer of dust on them. Use smaller, younger leaves.

Holly and Ivy Cough Syrup

(makes roughly 500ml)

30g of Holly leaves and 30g of young Ivy leaves finely chopped

Add spices like cardamom, star anise, cinnamon, Thyme, sage

Boil, then simmer for an hour. Strain and measure liquid.
Add sugar or honey using the ratio
1g sugar/honey : 1ml water.

Boil to thicken for 5 minutes.
Let cool then bottle in sterilised jars.
Label and keep in the fridge.

Dosage: For child 2.5 ml 2-3 x a day, Adult 5ml 3-4 x

Spicy "Immunity"-Infused Port

This is a very seasonal drink which you can just take a slug of
every day to help with supporting immunity.
It makes a good mid-winter present.

It is one part port or non-alcoholic ginger wine or any deep
coloured non-alcoholic juice like grape juice.

Mix together and add a pinch of Herb Bennett root (tastes like
cloves!), Echinacea root, Mallow root, Elderberries, Rosehips and
some spices like star anise, cardamom and cinnamon.

With all these recipes, you can use whatever you can
get hold of.

Simmer with these herbs for 40 minutes, strain and bottle.

Ivy and Holly

Gardening tips

Planting

Peruse seed & plant catalogues, plan your early moves for spring. Check your stock of saved seeds before you put in an order.

Garden Maintenance

Keep paths clear and clean to avoid slips and trips.

Collect leaves and pile them in corners for the overwintering bugs and beetles.

Put straw, bracken or leaves on tender plants and climbers to protect them. Continue bare-rooted planting of shrubs and bushes if weather permits.

Tidy the shed and sort your tools out. Clean, repair and oil the wooden handles, sharpen secateurs.

Reduce watering for all indoor plants: tricky in overheated houses so fine judgment is needed; all plants need a rest.

Wildlife

Melt ice on ponds and water baths for birds to drink. Put out water for them if there is no accessible water. Keep bird feeders filled up and clean.

More Information and Resources

Thoughts from a Covid gardener

My name is Josephine and I volunteer for HWBB. As I am 70 and 're-tired' I was lucky to be able to spend a lot of time in our HWBB herb allotment during lockdown. It was a good moment, as a professional gardener had recently levelled a piece of ground and made a retaining wall for some new beds. So, I decided to design and create these beds as well as maintain the garden with the help of other volunteers.

I ordered the plants, scouring the internet for Lovage, Hyssop and Coltsfoot. A lovely volunteer hauled beautiful bricks, I laid them out, and bought grit for the Hyssop. The flower lawn was created by two gardener volunteers, while I dug and weeded the old beds.

This work saved my life, giving me a sense of connection with cycles of gardening life, as well as exercise. The plants were going to make medicine and help other people, and were keeping me whole in mind and body too. Watching them respond to a little cosseting was like making a sick child well and happy. The digging, weeding, tending, and sowing allowed me time to realise how lucky I am simply to be alive; how privileged I am to do this work.

Because my normal round of jobs and doings were not possible and mainly involved people, I was forced to change and see what a marvel-lous resource the garden is in so many ways. My mind completely oc-cupied with the job in hand, my body moving, I felt part of a greater whole, I often sat exhausted after eating my lunch, watching the in-sects work the plants, fascinated.

Over a week I observed ants clear a sage bush of blackfly and learned that they milk them to drink the nectar, sometimes removing their wings to carry them to their nests for easy access. I treated ant nests with respect after that. I saw how many different bees and pollinators inhabit our space, loving the variety of flowers. A pair of robins became very demanding, especially when feeding their young, and was company when my allotment neighbour was not around.

I have an ancient, tattered gardening book published in the mid-20th century that belonged to my father. It contains Mr Middleton's sayings, and became my touch stone for things to be doing and looking out for in the garden.

According to RHS research, 27 million gardeners care for an area bigger than all of Great Britain's nature reserves put together. So we have a responsibility to the land we tend, and are doing more important work than we may think.

After my days in the herb allotment I went home on my bicycle and was able to say hello to friends and family at two metres' distance without feeling so sad.

Growing tips for some of the important herbs

Herb	Sow plant	Conditions	Harvest	Use
Comfrey (Perennial)	Grows from a bit of root anytime of year. Can become invasive.	Likes damp marshy places in the wild. Will grow anywhere.	Pick leaves from spring to autumn. Don't pick if they are mouldy. Unless for the compost heap.	Make infused oil for ointments, also to enrich the compost heap as well as for fertiliser.
Elderflower (Deciduous shrub/tree)	Find in wasteland and beside paths.	Likes sun but is shade-tolerant.	Creamy flowers in June and July. Dry as quickly as possible out of the sun.	Helps clear mucus and increase body temperature to help fight infections.
Blackcurrant (Deciduous shrub)	Plant in the autumn. Can be grown from cuttings.	Likes full sun and a good rich loam.	The buds and leaves in the spring and the berries when they are ripe in June and July.	Make syrups or oxymel to support immunity through the winter.
Passionflower (Climber)	Sow seed or plant in the spring, providing support.	A south to south-west wall or trellis. Any damp soil, likes dappled shade to full sun.	Pick flowers as they come out. Dry and store or use fresh.	For a calming cup of tea or tincture. Can aid sleep or calm anxiety.
Marshmallow (Perennial)	Sow seed in the spring, plant when big enough.	Likes moist ground and loamy soil in full sun.	Leaves and flower June onwards. 2 to 3 year roots in the autumn.	A soothing and healing herb for the respiratory and digestive systems.

Herb	Sow plant	Conditions	Harvest	Use
Angelica archangelica (Biennial)	Will self seed, or sow in the autumn for planting out the next year. May need staking.	Prefers rich damp soil and partial shade.	Dig 1st year roots in the Autumn, replanting some for next year.	Used to treat indigestion and soothe period pain.
Echinacea (Perennial)	Plant in the autumn.	Likes rich sandy soil in full sun but tolerant to most conditions.	Dig roots and rhizomes in autumn.	Supports the immune system to deal with infections e.g. colds and flu.
Holly (Perennial)	Grow from a hard-wood cutting in Nov/ Dec. Keep moist.	Likes well-drained but not dry, slightly acidic soil in full sun.	Gather young leaves in the spring and summer.	Use the leaves for a fever or a chesty cough.

Places to source seeds and herbs

- Organic Gardening Catalogue have different seed mixes for odd corners such as good mixed packets for birds and bees (*www.organiccatalogue.com*)

- Poyntzfield Herb Nursery (*www.poyntzfieldherbs.co.uk*)

- *Naturescape.co.uk* has really good plants and plugs, particularly for wild flowers

- Heritage Wildflowers in Norfolk for seeds (*www.heritagewildflowers.co.uk*)

- Jekkas Nursery *(www.jekkas.com)*

- Grow Wilder in Bristol have a huge selection of native wild plants for sale all year round *(www.avonwildlifetrust.org.uk/explore/grow-wilder)*

More on wildlife

- For a full and detailed list of ideal plants for pollinators, see the RHS Perfect for Pollinators list *(www.rhs.org.uk/perfectforpollinators)*

- RHS (Royal Horticultural Society) has lots of pictures and info on good and bad bugs.

- Bug Life - the Invertebrate Conservation Trust. *(www.buglife.org.uk)*

- Key insect pollinators of summer in the UK *(www.countryfile.com/wildlife/how-to-identify/key-pollinators-of-summer/)*

Recommended books

- Self Sufficient Herbalism by Lucy Jones
- Jekka's Complete Herb book by Jekka McVicar
- The Herb Garden Month by Month by Barbara Segall
- The Kew Gardener's Guide to Growing Herbs by Holly Farrell
- The Pollinator Victory Garden by Kim Eireman

Acknowledgements and image credits

This book has been a collective affair from the very first meeting where we ate pizza together on a rainy evening in Bristol and imagined it into existence. Since then there have been many meetings, much tea drunk (herbal of course), and many discussions. We have sat together in each other's gardens in summer with laptops on knees in productive flurries between family and work commitments.

We wish to extend our heartfelt thanks to everyone who has contributed. Thanks especially to all those who have donated recipes (credited in the main text), and artworks (credits below). We want to thank everyone who has been involved in any way - small or big way - for your help in making this book happen.

Writing and recipes

Becs Griffiths / rhizomeclinic.org.uk
Annwen Jones / rhizomeclinic.org.uk
Helen Rideout / helentheherb.com
Josephine Slater / bristolhwb.org

Contributions also from

Faith Morton
Polly Stansell
Shelly Abrahams
Alice Essam

Copy Editing

Drew Rose

Proofreading

Alice Essam
Jo McGain
Isy

Editing

Natalie Gill

Images

Front cover

Belle Benfield / www.bellebenfield.com

Introduction

Echinacea - Mo Barclay / moby5414@gmail.com
Hands - Nut Blossom / @nutblossom

Harvesting

Foraging basket and scythe - Elizabeth Crawford / @foraged_futures
Basket of flowers - Amani Omejer / @amani_writes

Gardening

St Werburghs medicine garden - HWB Bristol
Harvesting at the medicine garden - HWB Bristol
Seven starter herbs - Hannah Grace / hgrceoc.com
Rose - Evelyn Basch / evelynbasch.co.uk
Fork and spade / Elizabeth Crawford / @foraged_futures
Gardener - Hermione Skrine / hermione-skrine.co.uk

Medicine Making

Pestle and mortar / Elizabeth Crawford / @foraged_futures
Medicine making photos / Amani Omejer / @amani_writes

January

Oyster mushroom - Lucca Benney / @lucca.bucca
Turkey tail - Amani Omejer / @amani_writes
Garlic - Rosanna Morris / rosannamorris.com

February

Spruce - Nut Blossom / @nutblossom
Cleavers - Evelyn Polk / evelynpolk.vpweb.co.uk

March

Herbs photo / HWB Bristol
Dandelion - Kim Sweet / kimsweet.co.uk
Nettle - Rosanna Morris / rosannamorris.com
Birch tapping photo - rhizomeclinic.org.uk
Birch tree - Daniel Cox / @theanimist

April

Plantain - Amani Omejer / @amani_writes
Wild garlic - Amani Omejer / @amani_writes
Daisy - Kim Sweet / kimsweet.co.uk
Comfrey - Amani Omejer / @amani_writes

May

Elderflower - Frances Whitfield / francesmwhitfield@gmail.com
Elderflower medallion - Lucia Haluskova / facebook.com/oliviahaluskova
Hawthorn flowers - Kurda Yar / yarelawa@gmail.com
Rose - Evelyn Basch / evelynbasch.co.uk
Kelp - Rosie Barker
Eggwrack - Rosie Barker

June

Mugwort - Amani Omejer / @amani_writes
Calendula - Amani Omejer / @amani_writes
Blackcurrant - Libby Bove / libby.bove.letterbox@gmail.com
St Johns Wort & Lemon balm - Alex Goodman /
facebook.com/hopeanchorcollective
Vervain - Amani Omejer / @amani_writes

July

Passionflower - Cathy May / @vivalamy_art
Passionflower photo - Shelly Abrahams
Limeflower picking photo - Amani Omejer / @amani_writes
Limeflower - Amani Omejer / @amani_writes
Honeysuckle photo - Annwen Jones / rhizomeclinic.org.uk
Wood Betony - Amani Omejer / @amani_writes
Meadowsweet - Belle Benfield / bellebenfield.com

August

Yarrow - Rosanna Morris / rosannamorris.com
Marshmallow photo - Annwen Jones / rhizomeclinic.org.uk
Lavender - Kurda Yar / yarelawa@gmail.com
Blackberry - Holly Maslen / hollyvmaslen.com
Nettles with seeds - Belle Benfield / bellebenfield.com
Marshmallow - Nichola Goff / nicholagoff.com

September

Hops - Emma Leyfield / valerian.co.uk
Hawthorn berries - Amani Omejer / @amani_writes
Sea Buckthorn - Kurda Yar / yarelawa@gmail.com
Fennel - Amani Omejer / @amani_writes

October

Rosehips - Kurda Yar / yarelawa@gmail.com
Angelica - Belle Benfield / bellebenfield.co.uk
Dandelion and burdock - Sophie Gouk / sophie.wixsite.com/sophiegouk
Oyster mushroom - Lucca Benney / @lucca.bucca
Hen of the woods - Lucca Benney / @lucca.bucca

November

Echinacea - Mo Barclay / moby5414@gmail.com
Elecampane - Amani Omejer / @amani_writes

December

Spices photo - Annwen Jones / rhizomeclinic.org.uk
Horseradish - Rosanna Morris / rosannamorris.com
Holly & Ivy - Elisa Marconi / @elisa_thirteen

Book design

Tina Altwegg / wingedfoxdesigns.co.uk

How you could be involved

There are many ways that you can get involved with the project. We need volunteers to help with:

- Medicine making
- Growing & harvesting herbs
- Foraging for herbs that we need
- Drying & preparing herbs for storage
- Dispensary management & stock control
- Maintaining the Herbalists Without Borders, Bristol medicine garden
- Administration of the project: we welcome people with admin acumen particularly finance related skills.
- Translation and interpretive skills
- Visiting projects & delivering workshops
- Donating money

For more information, please get in touch with us below!

W: bristolhwb.org
E: hwb.bristol@gmail.com
F: www.facebook.com/bristolhwb/

Nettle root
Belle Benfield / www.bellebenfield.com